Poems of Spirit and Action

selected by W. M. Smyth, M.A.

Second Edition

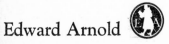

Edward Arnold

© W. M. Smyth 1971

First published 1957
by Edward Arnold (Publisher) Ltd.,
25 Hill Street,
London, W1X 8LL

Reprinted 1957 (twice), 1958 (twice), 1959, 1960, 1961, 1962 (twice),
1964 (twice), 1965 (twice), 1966 (twice), 1968, 1969, 1970
Second Edition 1971
Reprinted 1974

ISBN: 0 7131 1703 6

Printed in Great Britain by
Richard Clay (The Chaucer Press), Ltd.,
Bungay, Suffolk

Introduction

Poetry read in school should give pleasure to the pupils; practising teachers and educational theorists seem fairly well agreed that the sort of poetry that appeals to girls and boys in their early teens is poetry that tells a story.

This book is an attempt to compile an anthology that consists chiefly, though not entirely, of narrative verse; the poems in it that are not narrative are still vigorous and forthright in spirit. Each poem has been found by experience to compel the attention of girls and boys in junior forms—to be a poem sufficiently strong and direct to speak for itself to pupils of this age and to give them honest enjoyment.

Narrative poetry does not limit poetic experience unduly. Within these poems pupils will find more than the story : they will find the pleasures of sound, rhythm and imagery, they will feel the stir of emotion, they will develop fresh perceptions.

Several of the poems have brief introductory notes that are included with some hesitation. It seemed useful, however, to set before the reader some of the facts in the mind of the poet or something of the background of the poem. Apart from this, each poem is left to speak for itself.

Introduction to the Second Edition

This new edition, although redesigned and reset, remains the same book that has been used so widely and appreciated so much. The opportunity has been taken however, after this period of tremendous popularity, to remove one or two poems that now seem to have less impact and to replace them with poems written more recently.

Contents

ANIMALS

RAILWAYS

THE SEA

WARFARE

AGE AND DEATH

LONGER STORY POEMS

Not very serious

THE LAMA

Ogden Nash

The one-l lama,
He's a priest.
The two-l llama,
He's a beast.
And I will bet
A silk pyjama
There isn't any
Three-l lllama.

THE HIPPO

Hilaire Belloc

I shoot the Hippopotamus
With bullets made of platinum,
Because if I use leaden ones
His hide is sure to flatten 'em.

THE COMMON CORMORANT

Anonymous

The common cormorant or shag
Lays eggs inside a paper bag,
The reason you will see no doubt
It is to keep the lightning out.

But what these unobservant birds
Have never noticed is that herds
Of wandering bears may come with buns
And steal the bags to hold the crumbs.

HEAD AND HEART

C. D. B. Ellis

I put my hand upon my heart
And swore that we should never part—
I wonder what I should have said
If I had put it on my head.

ON THE NING NANG NONG

Spike Milligan

On the Ning Nang Nong
Where the cows go Bong!
And the monkeys all say Boo!
There's a Nong Nang Ning
Where the trees go Ping!
And the teapots Jibber Jabber Joo.
On the Nong Ning Nang
All the mice go clang!
And you just can't catch 'em when they do!
So it's Ning Nang Nong!
Cows go Bong!
Nong Nang Ning!
Trees go Ping!
Nong Ning Nang!
The mice go clang!
What a noisy place to belong
Is the Ning Nang Ning Nang Nong!

PEAS

Anonymous

I eat my peas with honey,
I've done it all my life.
It makes the peas taste funny,
But it keeps them on the knife.

Three epitaphs

MIKE O'DAY

Anonymous

This is the grave of Mike O'Day
Who died maintaining his right of way.
His right was clear, his will was strong,
But he's just as dead as if he'd been wrong.

EZRA POUND

Anonymous

Here lies the body of Ezra Pound,
Lost at sea and never was found.

MARTIN ELGINBRODDE

Anonymous

Here lie I, Martin Elginbrodde:
Ha'e mercy on my soul, Lord God,
As I wad do, were I Lord God
And ye were Martin Elginbrodde.

3

JABBERWOCKY

Lewis Carroll

This poem comes from 'Through the Looking Glass'. Alice found the poem printed backwards and read it by holding the book up in front of a mirror.

'Twas brillig, and the slithy toves
Did gyre and gimble in the wabe;
All mimsy were the borogoves,
And the mome raths outgrabe.

'Beware the Jabberwock, my son!
The jaws that bite, the claws that catch!
Beware the Jubjub bird and shun
The frumious Bandersnatch!'

He took his vorpal sword in hand:
Long time the manxome foe he sought—
So rested he by the Tumtum tree,
And stood awhile in thought.

And as in uffish thought he stood,
The Jabberwock, with eyes of flame,
Came whiffling through the tulgey wood,
And burbled as it came!

One, two! One, two! And through and through
The vorpal blade went snicker-snack!
He left it dead, and with its head
He went galumphing back.

'Now hast thou slain the Jabberwock!
Come to my arms, my beamish boy!
O frabjous day! Callooh Callay!
He chortled in his joy.

'Twas brillig, and the slithy toves
Did gyre and gimble in the wabe:
All mimsy were the borogoves,
And the mome raths outgrabe.

JIM
who ran away from his nurse, and was eaten by a lion

Hilaire Belloc

There was a Boy whose name was Jim.
His Friends were very good to him.
They gave him Tea, and Cakes, and Jam,
And slices of delicious Ham,
And Chocolate with pink inside,
And little Tricycles to ride,
And read him Stories through and through,
And even took him to the Zoo—
But there it was the dreadful Fate
Befell him, which I now relate.

You know—at least you ought to know,
For I have often told you so—
That Children never are allowed
To leave their Nurses in a Crowd;
Now this was Jim's especial Foible;
He ran away when he was able,
And on this inauspicious day
He slipped his hand and ran away!
He hadn't gone a yard when—Bang!
With open Jaws, a Lion sprang,
And hungrily began to eat
The boy: beginning at his feet.

Now, just imagine how it feels
When first your toes and then your heels,
And then by gradual degrees,
Your shins and ankles, calves and knees,
Are slowly eaten, bit by bit.
No wonder Jim detested it!
No wonder that he shouted 'Hi!'
The Honest Keeper heard his cry;
Though very fat he almost ran
To help the little gentleman.
'Ponto!' he ordered as he came
(For Ponto was the Lion's name),
'Ponto!' he cried, with angry Frown,
Let go, Sir! Down, Sir! Put it down!'

The Lion made a sudden Stop,
He let the Dainty Morsel drop,
And slunk reluctant to his Cage,
Snarling with Disappointed Rage.
But when he bent him over Jim,
The Honest Keeper's Eyes were dim.
The Lion having reached his Head,
The Miserable Boy was dead!
When Nurse informed his Parents, they
Were more Concerned than I can say:—
His Mother, as she dried her eyes,
Said, 'Well—it gives me no surprise,
He would not do as he was told!'
His Father, who was self-controlled,
Bade all the children round attend
To James's miserable end,
And always keep a-hold of Nurse
For fear of finding something worse.

POACHING IN EXCELSIS

G. K. Menzies

('*Two men were fined £120 apiece for poaching a white rhinoceros.*'
—*South African Press.*)

I've poached a pickel paitricks[1] when the leaves were turnin'
    sere,
I've poached a twa-three hares an' grouse, an' mebbe whiles a
    deer,
But ou, it seems an unco thing, an' jist a wee mysterious,
Hoo any mortal could contrive tae poach a rhinocerious.

I've crackit wi' the keeper, pockets packed wi' pheasants' eggs,
An' a ten-pun' saumon hangin' doun in baith my trouser legs,
But eh, I doot effects wud be a wee thing deleterious
Gin ye shuld stow intil yer breeks a brace o' rhinocerious.

I mind hoo me an' Wullie shot a Royal in Braemar,
An' brocht him doun tae Athol by the licht o' mune an' star.
An' eh, Sirs! but the canny beast contrived tae fash an' weary
    us—
Yet staigs maun be but bairn's play beside a rhinocerious.

---

[1] a brace of partridges.

I thocht I kent o' poachin' jist as muckle's ither men,
But there is still a twa-three things I doot I dinna ken;
An' noo I cannot rest, my brain is growin' that deleerious
Tae win awa' tae Africa an' poach a rhinocerious.

WILLIAM I – 1066

Eleanor and Herbert Farjeon

William the First was the first of our kings,
Not counting Ethelreds, Egberts and things,
And he had himself crowned and anointed and blest
In Ten-Sixty-I-Needn't-Tell-You-The-Rest.

But being a Norman, King William the First
By the Saxons he conquered was hated and cursed,
And they planned and they plotted far into the night,
Which William could tell by the candles alight.

Then William decided these rebels to quell
By ringing the Curfew, a sort of a bell,
And if any Saxon was found out of bed
After eight o'clock sharp, it was Off With His Head!

So at BONG NUMBER ONE they all started to run
Like a warren of rabbits upset by a gun;
At BONG NUMBER TWO they were all in a stew,
Flinging cap after tunic and hose after shoe;
At BONG NUMBER THREE they were bare to the knee,
Undoing the doings as quick as could be;
At BONG NUMBER FOUR they were stripped to the core,
And pulling on nightshirts the wrong side before;
At BONG NUMBER FIVE they were looking alive,
And bizzing and buzzing like bees in a hive;
At BONG NUMBER SIX they gave themselves kicks,
Tripping over the rushes to snuff out the wicks;
At BONG NUMBER SEVEN, from Durham to Devon,
They slipped up a prayer to Our Father in Heaven;
And at BONG NUMBER EIGHT it was fatal to wait,
So with hearts beating all at a terrible rate,
In the deuce of a state, I need hardly relate,
They jumped Bong into bed like a bull at a gate.

MACAVITY: THE MYSTERY CAT

T. S. Eliot

Macavity's a Mystery Cat: he's called the Hidden Paw—
For he's the master criminal who can defy the Law.
He's the bafflement of Scotland Yard, the Flying Squad's
    despair:
For when they reach the scene of crime—Macavity's not there!

Macavity, Macavity, there's no one like Macavity,
He's broken every human law, he breaks the law of gravity.
His powers of levitation would make a fakir stare,
And when you reach the scene of crime—Macavity's not there!
You may seek him in the basement, you may look up in the
    air—
But I tell you once and once again, Macavity's not there!

Macavity's a ginger cat, he's very tall and thin;
You would know him if you saw him, for his eyes are sunken
    in.
His brow is deeply lined with thought, his head is highly
    domed;
His coat is dusty from neglect, his whiskers are uncombed.
He sways his head from side to side, with movements like a
    snake;
And when you think he's half asleep, he's always wide awake.

Macavity, Macavity, there's no one like Macavity.
For he's a fiend in feline shape, a monster of depravity.
You may meet him in a by-street, you may see him in the
    square—
But when a crime's discovered, then Macavity's not there!

He's outwardly respectable. (They say he cheats at cards.)
And his footprints are not found in any file of Scotland Yard's.
And when the larder's looted, or the jewel-case is rifled,
Or when the milk is missing, or another Peke's been stifled,
Or the greenhouse glass is broken, and the trellis past repair—
Ay, there's the wonder of the thing! Macavity's not there!

And when the Foreign Office find a Treaty's gone astray,
Or the Admiralty lose some plans and drawings by the way,
There may be a scrap of paper in the hall or on the stair—
But it's useless to investigate—Macavity's not there!
And when the loss has been disclosed, the Secret Service say:
'It must have been Macavity!'—but he's a mile away.
You'll be sure to find him resting, or a-licking of his thumbs,
Or engaged in doing complicated long division sums.

Macavity, Macavity, there's no one like Macavity,
There never was a Cat of such deceitfulness and suavity.
He always has an alibi, and one or two to spare:
At whatever time the deed took place—Macavity wasn't there!
And they say that all the Cats whose wicked deeds are widely
    known
(I might mention Mungojerrie, I might mention Griddlebone)
Are nothing more than agents for the Cat who all the time
Just controls their operations: the Napoleon of Crime.

THE DAVID JAZZ

Edward Meade Robinson

David was a Young Blood, David was a striplin',
Looked like the Jungle Boy, yarned about by Kiplin'—
Looked like a Jungle Boy, sang like a bird,
Fought like a tiger when his temper got stirred.
David was a-tendin' the sheep for his Pa,
Somebody hollered to him—that was his Ma—
'Run down to camp with this little bitta snack,
Give it to your brothers, an' hurry right back.'

David took the lunchbox, and off he hurried;
There he saw the Isra'lites lookin' right worried.
Asked 'em what's the matter—they pointed to the Prairie—
There he saw a sight to make an Elephant scary!
There he saw Goliath,
Champion o' Gath,
Howlin' in his anger,
Roarin' in his wrath;
Stronger than a lion,
Taller than a tree—

9

David had to tip-toe to reach to his knee!
'Come on,' says the Giant, a-ragin' and a-stridin'—
'Drag out your champions from the holes where they're hidin',
Drag out your strong men from underneath their bunks,
And I'll give 'em to the buzzards, an' the lizzards, an' the
     skunks!'

David heard him braggin', and he said, 'I declare,
The great big lummox got 'em buffaloed for fair.'
Goes to the brook, and he picks him out a pebble,
Smooth as a goose-egg an' hard as the debbil.
Starts for the giant, dancin' on his toes,
Whirlin' his sling-shot and singin' as he goes—
'Better get organized, for here I come a-hoppin',
Time's gettin' short, and hell am a-poppin'.
Hell am a-poppin' and trouble am a-brewin',
Nothing's going to save you from Big Red Ruin.
Trouble am a-brewin' and Death am distillin'—
Look out, you Philistine—there's gwineter be a killin'!'
Giant looks at David an' he lets out a laugh,—
Acts like a tiger bein' sassed by a calf;
Laughs like a hyena, grins from ear to ear,
Rattles on his armor with his ten-foot spear,
Starts out for David, bangin' and a-clankin'—
'Come on, l'il infant, you're a goin' to get a spankin'!'
David takes his sling shot, swings it round his head,
Lets fly a pebble—and the gi'nt drops dead!

Moral

Big men, little men, houses and cars,
Widders and winders and porcelain jars—
Nothin' ain't safe from damage an' shocks,
When the neighborhood chillen gets to slingin' rocks!

ADVENTURES OF ISABEL

Ogden Nash

Isabel met an enormous bear;
Isabel, Isabel, didn't care.
The bear was hungry, the bear was ravenous,
The bear's big mouth was cruel and cavernous.

The bear said, Isabel, glad to meet you,
How do, Isabel, now I'll eat you!
Isabel, Isabel, didn't worry,
Isabel didn't scream or scurry.
She washed her hands and she straightened her hair up,
Then Isabel quietly ate the bear up.

Once on a night as black as pitch
Isabel met a wicked old witch.
The witch's face was cross and wrinkled,
The witch's gums with teeth were sprinkled.
Ho, ho, Isabel! the old witch crowed,
I'll turn you into an ugly toad!
Isabel, Isabel, didn't worry,
Isabel didn't scream or scurry.
She showed no rage and she showed no rancour,
But she turned the witch into milk and drank her.

Isabel met a hideous giant,
Isabel continued self-reliant.
The giant was hairy, the giant was horrid,
He had one eye in the middle of his forehead.
Good morning, Isabel, the giant said,
I'll grind your bones to make my bread.
Isabel, Isabel, didn't worry,
Isabel didn't scream or scurry.
She nibbled the zwieback[1] that she always fed off,
And when it was gone, she cut the giant's head off.

Isabel met a troublesome doctor,
He punched and he poked till he really shocked her.
The doctor's talk was of coughs and chills
And the doctor's satchel bulged with pills.
The doctor said unto Isabel,
Swallow this, it will make you well.
Isabel, Isabel, didn't worry,
Isabel didn't scream or scurry.
She took those pills from the pill-concocter,
And Isabel calmly cured the doctor.

---

[1] Biscuit.

SONG TO BE SUNG BY THE FATHER OF INFANT FEMALE CHILDREN

Ogden Nash

My heart leaps up when I behold
A rainbow in the sky;
Contrariwise, my blood runs cold
When little boys go by.
For little boys as little boys
No special hate I carry,
But now and then they grow to men,
And when they do, they marry.
No matter how they tarry,
Eventually they marry.
And, swine among the pearls,
They marry little girls.

Oh, somewhere, somewhere, an infant plays,
With parents who feed and clothe him.
Their lips are sticky with pride and praise,
But I have begun to loathe him.
Yes, I loathe with a loathing shameless
This child who to me is nameless.
This bachelor child in his carriage
Gives never a thought to marriage,
But a person can hardly say knife
Before he will hunt him a wife.

I never see an infant (male),
A-sleeping in the sun,
Without I turn a trifle pale
And think, is *he* the one?
Oh, first he'll want to crop his curls,
And then he'll want a pony,
And then he'll think of pretty girls
And holy matrimony.
He'll put away his pony,
And sigh for matrimony.
A cat without a mouse
Is he without a spouse.

Oh, somewhere he bubbles bubbles of milk,
And quietly sucks his thumbs;
His cheeks are roses painted on silk,
And his teeth are tucked in his gums.
But alas, the teeth will begin to grow,
And the bubbles will cease to bubble;
Given a score of years or so,
The roses will turn to stubble.
He'll sell a bond, or he'll write a book,
And his eyes will get that acquisitive look,
And raging and ravenous for the kill,
He'll boldly ask for the hand of Jill.

This infant whose middle
Is diapered still
Will want to marry
My daughter Jill.

Oh sweet be his slumber and moist his middle!
My dreams, I fear, are infanticiddle.
A fig for embryo Lohengrins!
I'll open all of his safety pins,
I'll pepper his powder and salt his bottle,
And give him readings from Aristotle,
Sand for his spinach I'll gladly bring,
And tabasco sauce for his teething ring,
And an elegant, elegant alligator
To play with in his perambulator.
Then perhaps he'll struggle through fire and water
To marry somebody else's daughter!

Pirates and smugglers

SPANISH WATERS

John Masefield

The Caribbean Sea and the West Indies became the hunting-ground of pirates and, hence, the scene of so many adventure stories. It was not until the nineteenth century that the navies of England and the United States established control over these waters and brought to an end the days of 'story-book' piracy.

Spanish waters, Spanish waters, you are ringing in my ears,
Like a slow sweet piece of music from the grey forgotten years;
Telling tales, and beating tunes, and bringing weary thoughts to
    me
Of the sandy beach at Muertos, where I would that I could be.

There's a surf breaks on Los Muertos, and it never stops to
    roar,
And it's there we came to anchor, and it's there we went
    ashore,
Where the blue lagoon is silent amid snags of rotting trees,
Dropping like the clothes of corpses cast up by the seas.

We anchored at Los Muertos when the dipping sun was red,
We left her half-a-mile to sea, to west of Nigger Head;
And before the mist was on the Cay, before the day was done,
We were all ashore on Muertos with gold that we had won.

We bore it through the marshes in a half-score battered chests,
Sinking, in the sucking quagmires, to the sunburn on our
    breasts.
Heaving over tree-trunks, gasping, damning at the flies and
    heat,
Longing for a long drink, out of silver, in the ship's cool
    lazareet.

The moon came white and ghostly as we laid the treasure
    down,
There was gear there'd make a beggarman as rich as Lima
    Town,
Copper charms and silver trinkets from the chests of Spanish
    crews,
Gold doubloons and double moidores, louis d'ors and portagues,

Clumsy yellow-metal earrings from the Indians of Brazil,
Uncut emeralds out of Rio, bezoar stones from Guayaquil;
Silver, in the crude and fashioned, pots of old Arica bronze,
Jewels from the bones of Incas desecrated by the Dons.

We smoothed the place with mattocks, and we took and blazed
    the tree,
Which marks yon where the gear is hid that none will ever see,
And we laid aboard the ship again, and south away we steers,
Through the loud surf of Los Muertos which is beating in my
    ears.

I'm the last alive that knows it. All the rest have gone their
    ways,
Killed, or died, or come to anchor in the old Mulatas Cays,
And I go singing, fiddling, old and starved and in despair,
And I know where all that gold is hid, if I were only there.

It's not the way to end it all. I'm old, and nearly blind,
And an old man's past's a strange thing, for it never leaves his
    mind.
And I see in dreams, awhiles, the beach, the sun's disc dipping
    red,
And the tall ship, under topsails, swaying in past Nigger Head.

I'd be glad to step ashore there. Glad to take a pick and go
To the lone blazed coco-palm tree in the place no others know,
And lift the gold and silver that has mouldered there for years
By the loud surf of Los Muertos which is beating in my ears.

A DUTCH PICTURE

Henry Wadsworth Longfellow

*When the power of Spain declined, the Dutch rivalled the English
as sea-dogs or merchant-adventurers—buccaneers or pirates if you
like. Longfellow describes a Dutch captain, living in retirement
with his booty and his memories, one who still feels the call of the
sea.*

Simon Danz has come home again,
From cruising about with his buccaneers;
He has singed the beard of the King of Spain,
And carried away the Dean of Jaen
And sold him in Algiers.

In his house by the Maese, with its roof of tiles
And weathercocks flying aloft in air,
There are silver tankards of antique styles,
Plunder of convent and castle, and piles
Of carpets rich and rare.

In his tulip garden there by the town,
Overlooking the sluggish stream,
With his Moorish cap and dressing gown,
The old sea-captain, hale and brown,
Walks in a waking dream.

A smile in his gray mustachio lurks
Whenever he thinks of the King of Spain;
And the listed tulips look like Turks,
And the silent gardener as he works
Is changed to the Dean of Jaen.

The windmills on the outermost
Verge of the landscape in the haze,
To him are towers on the Spanish coast,
With whiskered sentinels at their post,
Though this is the river Maese.

But when the winter rains begin,
He sits and smokes by the blazing brands,
And old seafaring men come in,
Goat-bearded, gray, and with double chin,
And rings upon their hands.

They sit there in the shadow and shine
Of the flickering fire of the winter night;
Figures in colour and design
Like those by Rembrandt of the Rhine,
Half darkness and half light.

And they talk of ventures lost or won,
And their talk is ever and ever the same,
While they drink the red wine of Tarragon,
From the cellars of some Spanish Don,
Or convent set on flame.

Restless at times with heavy strides
He paces his parlour to and fro;
He is like a ship that at anchor rides,
And swings with the rising and falling tides,

And tugs at her anchor tow.

Voices mysterious far and near,
Sound of the wind and sound of the sea,
Are calling and whispering in his ear,
'Simon Danz! Why stayest thou here?
Come forth and follow me!'

So he thinks he shall take to the sea again
For one more cruise with his buccaneers,
To singe the beard of the King of Spain,
And capture another Dean of Jaen
And sell him in Algiers.

THE LAST BUCCANEER

Charles Kingsley

Oh, England is a pleasant place for them that's rich and high,
But England is a cruel place for such poor folks as I;
And such a port of mariners I ne'er shall see again,
As the pleasant Isle of Avès, beside the Spanish Main.

There were forty craft in Avès that were both swift and stout,
All furnished well with small arms and cannons round about;
And a thousand men in Avès made laws so fair and free
To choose their valiant captains and obey them loyally.

Thence we sailed against the Spaniard with his hoards of plate
     and gold,
Which he wrung with cruel tortures from Indian folk of old;
Likewise the merchant captains, with hearts as hard as stone,
Who flog men and keel-haul them, and starve them to the bone.

Oh, the palms grew high in Avès, and fruits that shone like gold,
And the colibris and parrots they were gorgeous to behold;
And the negro maids to Avès from bondage fast did flee,
To welcome gallant sailors, a-sweeping in from sea.

Oh, sweet it was in Avès to hear the landward breeze,
A-swing with good tobacco in a net between the trees,
With a negro lass to fan you, while you listened to the roar
Of the breakers on the reef outside, that never touched the
     shore.

But Scripture saith, an ending to all fine things must be;
So the King's ships sailed on Avès, and quite put down were
    we.
All day we fought like bulldogs, but they burst the booms at
    night,
And I fled in a piragua, sore wounded, from the fight.

Nine days I floated starving, and a negro lass beside,
Till for all I tried to cheer her, the poor young thing she died;
But as I lay a-gasping, a Bristol sail came by,
And brought me home to England here, to beg until I die.

And now I'm old and going—I'm sure I can't tell where;
One comfort is, this world's so hard, I can't be worse off there;
If I might but be a sea-dove, I'd fly across the main,
To the pleasant Isle of Avès, to look at it once again.

A SMUGGLER'S SONG

Rudyard Kipling

*Smuggling goods into England reached a climax, perhaps, in the
early nineteenth century, the time of the Napoleonic Wars. Most
of the adventure stories about smugglers deal with this period. It
was the task of the 'Revenue men' to prevent smuggling and to
ensure that prohibited goods were not imported at all and that other
goods were duly taxed.*

   *The poem comes from a book of short stories entitled 'Puck of
Pook's Hill'.*

If you wake at midnight, and hear a horse's feet,
Don't go drawing back the blind, or looking in the street,
Them that asks no questions isn't told a lie.
Watch the wall, my darling, while the Gentlemen go by!
Five and twenty ponies
Trotting through the dark—
Brandy for the Parson,
'Baccy for the Clerk;
Laces for a lady, letters for a spy,
And watch the wall, my darling, while the Gentlemen go by!

Running round the woodlump if you chance to find
Little barrels, roped and tarred, all full of brandy-wine,
Don't you shout to come and look, nor use 'em for your play.
Put the brushwood back again—and they'll be gone next day!

If you see the stable-door setting open wide;
If you see a tired horse lying down inside;
If your mother mends a coat cut about and tore;
If the lining's wet and warm—don't you ask no more!

If you meet King George's men, dressed in blue and red,
You be careful what you say, and mindful what is said,
If they call you 'pretty maid', and chuck you 'neath the chin,
Don't you tell where no one is, nor yet where no one's been!

Knocks and footsteps round the house—whistles after dark—
You've no call for running out till the house-dogs bark.
Trusty's here, and *Pincher's* here, and see how dumb they lie—
They don't fret to follow when the Gentlemen go by!
If you do as you've been told, 'likely there's a chance,
You'll be give a dainty doll, all the way from France,
With a cap of Valenciennes, and a velvet hood—
A present from the Gentlemen, along o' being good!
Five and twenty ponies
Trotting through the dark—
Brandy for the Parson,
'Baccy for the Clerk.
Them that asks no questions isn't told a lie—
Watch the wall, my darling, while the Gentlemen go by.

Stories in verse

SHAMEFUL DEATH

William Morris

There were four of us about that bed;
The mass-priest knelt at the side,
I and his mother stood at the head,
Over his feet lay the bride;
We were quite sure that he was dead,
Through his eyes were open wide.

He did not die in the night,
He did not die in the day,
But in the morning twilight
His spirit passed away,
When neither sun nor moon was bright,
And the trees were merely grey.

He was not slain with the sword,
Knight's axe, or the knightly spear,
Yet spoke he never a word
After he came in here;
I cut away the cord
From the neck of my brother dear.

He did not strike one blow,
For the recreants came behind,
In a place where the hornbeams grow,
A path right hard to find,
For the hornbeam boughs swing so,
That the twilight makes it blind.

They lighted a great torch then,
When his arms were pinioned fast.
Sir John the knight of the Fen,
Sir Guy of the Dolorous Blast,
With knights threescore and ten,
Hung brave Lord Hugh at last.

I am threescore and ten,
And my hair is all turned grey,
But I met Sir John of the Fen
Long ago on a summer day.
And am glad to think of the moment when
I took his life away.

I am threescore and ten,
And my strength is mostly passed,
But long ago I and my men,
When the sky was overcast,
And the smoke rolled over the reeds of the fen,
Slew Guy of the Dolorous Blast.

And now, knights all of you,
I pray you pray for Sir Hugh,
A good knight and a true,
And for Alice, his wife, pray too.

THE CASTLE

Edwin Muir

All through the summer at ease we lay,
And daily from the turret wall
We watched the mowers in the hay
And the enemy half a mile away;
They seemed no threat to us at all.

For what, we thought, had we to fear
With our arms and provender, load on load,
Our towering battlements, tier on tier,
And friendly allies drawing near
On every leafy summer road.

Our gates were strong, our walls were thick,
So smooth and high, no man could win
A foothold there, no clever trick
Could take us, have us dead or quick,
Only a bird could have got in.

What could they offer us for bait?
Our captain was brave and we were true...
There was a little private gate,
A little wicked wicket gate.
The wizened warder let them through.

Oh then our maze of tunnelled stone
Grew thin and treacherous as air,
The cause was lost without a groan,
The famous citadel overthrown,
And all its secret galleries bare.

How can this shameful tale be told?
I will maintain until my death
We could do nothing, being sold;
Our only enemy was gold,
And we had no arms to fight it with.

LOCHINVAR

Sir Walter Scott

Sir Walter Scott wrote this as part of a long poem called 'Marmion'. It is based on a very ancient ballad called 'Katarine Janfarie'.

O, Young Lochinvar is come out of the west,
Through all the wide Border his steed was the best;
And save his good broadsword he weapons had none,
He rode all unarm'd, and he rode all alone.
So faithful in love, and so dauntless in war,
There never was knight like the young Lochinvar.

He staid not for brake, and he stopp'd not for stone,
He swam the Eske river where ford there was none;
But ere he alighted at Netherby gate,
The bride had consented, the gallant came late:
For a laggard in love, and a dastard in war,
Was to wed the fair Ellen of brave Lochinvar.

So boldly he enter'd the Netherby Hall,
Among bride's-men, and kinsmen, and brothers, and all:
Then spoke the bride's father, his hand on his sword,
(For the poor craven bridegroom said never a word),
'O come ye in peace here, or come ye in war,
Or to dance at our bridal, young Lord Lochinvar?'

'I long woo'd your daughter, my suit you denied;
Love swells like the Solway, but ebbs like its tide—
And now am I come, with this lost love of mine,
To lead but one measure, drink one cup of wine.
There are maidens in Scotland more lovely by far,
That would gladly be bride to the young Lochinvar.'

The bride kiss'd the goblet: the knight took it up,
He quaff'd off the wine, and he threw down the cup.
She look'd down to blush, and she look'd up to sigh,
With a smile on her lips, and a tear in her eye.
He took her soft hand ere her mother could bar,—
'Now tread we a measure!' said young Lochinvar.

So stately his form, and so lovely her face,
That never a hall such a galliard did grace;
While her mother did fret, and her father did fume,
And the bridegroom stood dangling his bonnet and plume;
And the bride-maidens whisper'd, ' 'Twere better by far,
To have match'd our fair cousin with young Lochinvar.'

One touch to her hand, and one word in her ear,
When they reach'd the hall-door, and the charger stood near;
So light to the croupe the fair lady he swung,
So light to the saddle before her he sprung!
'She is won! we are gone, over bank, bush, and scaur;
They'll have fleet steeds that follow,' quoth young Lochinvar.

There was mounting 'mong Graemes of the Netherby clan;
Forsters, Fenwicks, and Musgraves, they rode and they ran;
There was racing and chasing on Cannobie Lee,
But the lost bride of Netherby ne'er did they see.
So daring in love, and so dauntless in war,
Have ye e'er heard of gallant like young Lochinvar?

HOW THEY BROUGHT THE GOOD NEWS FROM GHENT TO AIX

Robert Browning

I sprang to the stirrup, and Joris, and he;
I galloped, Dirck galloped, we galloped all three;
'Good speed!' cried the watch, as the gate-bolts undrew;
'Speed!' echoed the wall to us galloping through;
Behind shut the postern, the lights sank to rest,
And into the midnight we galloped abreast.

Not a word to each other; we kept the great pace
Neck by neck, stride by stride, never changing our place;
I turned in my saddle and made its girths tight,
Then shortened each stirrup, and set the pique right,
Rebuckled the cheek-strap, chained slacker the bit,
Nor galloped less steadily Roland a whit.

'Twas moonset at starting; but while we drew near
Lokeren, the cocks crew and twilight dawned clear;
At Boom, a great yellow star came out to see;
At Duffeld, 'twas morning as plain as could be;
And from Mecheln church-steeple we heard the half-chime,
So, Joris broke silence with, 'Yet there is time!'

At Aershot, up leaped of a sudden the sun,
And against him the cattle stood black every one,
To stare thro' the mist at us galloping past,
And I saw my stout galloper Roland at last,
With resolute shoulders, each butting away
The haze, as some bluff river headland its spray:

And his low head and crest, just one sharp ear bent back
For my voice, and the other pricked out on his track;
And one eye's black intelligence,—ever that glance
O'er its white edge at me, his own master, askance!
And the thick heavy spume-flakes which aye and anon
His fierce lips shook upwards in galloping on.

By Hasselt, Dirck groaned; and cried Joris, 'Stay spur!
Your Roos galloped bravely, the fault's not in her,
We'll remember at Aix'—for one heard the quick wheeze

Of her chest, saw the stretched neck and staggering knees,
And sunk tail, and horrible heave of the flank,
As down on her haunches she shuddered and sank.

So, we were left galloping, Joris and I,
Past Looz and past Tongres, no cloud in the sky;
The broad sun above laughed a pitiless laugh,
'Neath our feet broke the brittle bright stubble like chaff;
Till over by Dalhem a dome-spire sprang white,
And 'Gallop,' gasped Joris, 'for Aix is in sight!'

'How they'll greet us!'—and all in a moment his roan
Rolled neck and croup over, lay dead as a stone;
And there was my Roland to bear the whole weight
Of the news which alone could save Aix from her fate,
With his nostrils like pits full of blood to the brim,
And with circles of red for his eye-sockets' rim.

Then I cast loose my buffcoat, each holster let fall,
Shook off both my jack-boots, let go belt and all,
Stood up in the stirrup, leaned, patted his ear,
Called my Roland his pet-name, my horse without peer;
Clapped my hands, laughed and sang, any noise, bad or good,
Till at length into Aix Roland galloped and stood.

And all I remember is—friends flocking round
As I sat with his head 'twixt my knees on the ground;
And no voice but was praising this Roland of mine,
As I poured down his throat our last measure of wine,
Which (the burgesses voted by common consent)
Was no more than his due who brought good news from
     Ghent.

DICKENS IN CAMP

Bret Harte

*Bret Harte, an American poet, lived in California at the time of the
gold rush, about a hundred years ago.*
  *The novel referred to in this poem is 'The Old Curiosity Shop',
the pathetic story of the wanderings of Little Nell and her grand-
father.*

Above the pines the moon was slowly drifting,
The river sang below;
The dim sierras, far beyond, uplifting
Their minarets of snow.

The roaring camp-fire, with rude humour, painted
The ruddy tints of health
On haggard face and form that drooped and fainted
In the fierce race for wealth.

Till one arose, and from his pack's scant treasure
A hoarded volume drew,
And cards were dropped from hands of listless leisure
To hear the tale anew.

And then, while round them shadows gathered faster,
And as the firelight fell,
He read aloud the book wherein the Master
Had writ of 'Little Nell'.

Perhaps 'twas boyish fancy—for the reader
Was youngest of them all—
But, as he read, from clustering pine and cedar
A silence seemed to fall;

The fir-trees, gathering closer in the shadows,
Listened in every spray,
While the whole camp with 'Nell' on English meadows
Wandered, and lost their way.

And so in mountain solitudes—o'ertaken
As by some spell divine—
Their cares drop from them like the needles shaken
From out the gusty pine.

Lost is that camp, and wasted all its fire;
And he who wrought that spell?—
Ah, towering pine and stately Kentish spire,
Ye have one tale to tell!

Lost is that camp! but let its fragrant story
Blend with the breath that thrills
With hop-vines' incense all the pensive glory
That fills the Kentish hills.

And on that grave where English oak and holly
And laurel wreaths entwine,
Deem it not all a too presumptuous folly—
This spray of Western pine!

NANCY HANKS

Rosemary Benét

Nancy Hanks was the mother of Abraham Lincoln. Her husband, Thomas Lincoln, lived first in Kentucky and then in Indiana at a time when these were frontier states. Her last home, 'a half-faced camp', was a hut with only three sides and her family was brought up in hardships that we cannot picture. She died in 1818.

Her son, Abraham, grew up to become President of the United States of America at the time of the American Civil War, when slavery was a cause of dissension between the northern and southern states and when men resorted to arms to decide whether or not states could break away from the Union. Lincoln gave his country the leadership it needed, and he is regarded as one of the great men in the history of the world.

If Nancy Hanks
Came back as a ghost,
Seeking news
Of what she loved most,
She'd ask first
'Where's my son?
What's happened to Abe?
What's he done?

'Poor little Abe,
Left all alone
Except for Tom,
Who's a rolling stone
He was only nine
The year I died.
I remember still
How hard he cried.

'Scraping along
In a little shack,
With hardly a shirt
To cover his back,
And a prairie wind
To blow him down,
Or pinching times
If he went to town.

'You wouldn't know
About my son?
Did he grow tall?
Did he have fun?
Did he learn to read?
Did he get to town?
Do you know his name?
Did he get on?'

THE SICK STOCKRIDER

Adam Lindsay Gordon

*The writer of this poem lived in Australia in the sixties of last
century. This was the period when sheep-runs were being developed
and when gold discoveries had been made—hence the stockriders
and bushrangers.*

*In many ways 'the sick stockrider' may be identified with the
poet himself, who was probably writing of his own experiences.*

Hold hard, Ned! Lift me down once more, and lay me in the
　　shade.
Old man, you've had your work cut out to guide
Both horses, and to hold me in the saddle when I sway'd,
All through the hot, slow, sleepy, silent ride.
The dawn at 'Moorabinda' was a mist-rack dull and dense,
The sunrise was a sullen, sluggish lamp;
I was dozing in the gateway at Arbuthnot's bound'ry fence,
I was dreaming on the Limestone cattle camp.

We cross'd the creek at Carricksford, and sharply through the
　　haze,
And suddenly the sun shot flaming forth;

To southward lay 'Katawa', with the sand peaks all ablaze,
And the flush'd fields of Glen Lomond lay to north.
Now westward winds the bridle path that leads to Lindisfarm,
And yonder looms the double-headed Bluff;
From the far side of the first hill, when the skies are clear and
 calm,
You can see Sylvester's woolshed fair enough.
Five miles we used to call it from our homestead to the place
Where the big tree spans the roadway like an arch;
'Twas here we ran the dingo down that gave us such a chase
Eight years ago—or was it nine?—last March.

'Twas merry in the glowing morn, among the gleaming grass,
To wander as we've wander'd many a mile,
And blow the cool tobacco cloud, and watch the white wreaths
 pass,
Sitting loosely in the saddle all the while.
'Twas merry 'mid the blackwoods, when we spied the station
 roofs,
To wheel the wild scrub cattle at the yard,
With a running fire of stockwhips and a fiery run of hoofs;
O! the hardest day was never then too hard!

Aye! we had a glorious gallop after 'Starlight' and his gang,
When they bolted from Sylvester's on the flat;
How the sun-dried reed-beds crackled, how the flintstrewn
 ranges rang
To the strokes of 'Mountaineer' and 'Acrobat'.
Hard behind them in the timber, harder still across the heath,
Close beside them through the tea-tree scrub we dash'd;
And the golden-tinted fern leaves, how they rustled under-
 neath!
And the honeysuckle osiers, how they crash'd!

We led the hunt throughout, Ned, on the chestnut and the
 grey,
And the troopers were three hundred yards behind,
While we emptied our six-shooters on the bushrangers at bay,
In the creek with stunted box-tree for a blind!
There you grappled with the leader, man to man and horse to
 horse,
And you roll'd together when the chestnut rear'd;
He blazed away and missed you in that shallow watercourse—
A narrow shave—his powder singed your beard!

In these hours when life is ebbing, how those days when life
    was young
Come back to us; how clearly I recall
Even the yarns Jack Hall invented, and the songs Jem Roper
    sung;
And where are now Jem Roper and Jack Hall?
Aye! nearly all our comrades of the old colonial school,
Our ancient boon companions, Ned, are gone;
Hard livers for the most part, somewhat reckless as a rule;
It seems that you and I are left alone.

There was Hughes, who got in trouble through that business
    with the cards,
It matters little what became of him;
But a steer ripp'd up MacPherson in the Cooraminta yards,
And Sullivan was drown'd at Sink-or-swim;
And Mostyn—poor Frank Mostyn—died at last a fearful
    wreck,
In the 'horrors', at the Upper Wandinong,
And Carisbrooke, the rider, at the Horsefall broke his neck,
Faith! the wonder was he saved his neck so long!

Ah! those days and nights we squander'd at the Logans' in the
    glen—
The Logans, man and wife, have long been dead.
Elsie's tallest girl seems taller than your little Elsie then;
And Ethel is a woman grown and wed.

I've had my share of pastime, and I've done my share of toil,
And life is short—the longest life a span;
I care not now to tarry for the corn or for the oil,
Or the wine that maketh glad the heart of man.
For good undone and gifts misspent and resolutions vain,
'Tis somewhat late to trouble. This I know—
I should live the same life over, if I had to live again;
And the chances are I go where most men go.

The deep blue skies wax dusty, and the tall green trees grow
    dim,
The sward beneath me seems to heave and fall;
And sickly, smoky shadows through the sleepy sunlight swim,
And on the very sun's face weave their pall.

Let me slumber in the hollow where the wattle blossoms wave,
With never stone or rail to fence my bed;
Should the sturdy station children pull the bush flowers on my
    grave,
I may chance to hear them romping overhead.

THE BALLAD OF WILLIAM SYCAMORE

Stephen Vincent Benét

My father, he was a mountaineer,
His fist was a knotty hammer;
He was quick on his feet as a running deer,
And he spoke with a Yankee stammer.

My mother, she was merry and brave,
And so she came to her labour,
With a tall green fir for her doctor grave
And a stream for her comforting neighbour.

And some are wrapped in the linen fine,
And some like a godling's scion;
But I was cradled on twigs of pine
In the skin of a mountain lion.

And some remember a white, starched lap
And a ewer with silver handles;
But I remember a coonskin cap
And the smell of bayberry candles.

The cabin logs, with the bark still rough,
And my mother who laughed at trifles,
And the tall, lank visitors, brown as snuff,
With their long, straight squirrel-rifles.

I can hear them dance, like a foggy song,
Through the deepest one of my slumbers,
The fiddle squeaking the boots along
And my father calling the numbers.

The quick feet shaking the puncheon-floor,
The fiddle squeaking and squealing,
Till the dried herbs rattled above the door
And the dust went up to the ceiling.

There are children lucky from dawn till dusk,
But never a child so lucky!
For I cut my teeth on 'Money Musk'
In the Bloody Ground of Kentucky!

When I grew tall as the Indian corn,
My father had little to lend me,
But he gave me his great, old powder-horn
And his woodsman's skill to befriend me.

With a leather shirt to cover my back,
And a redskin nose to unravel
Each forest sign, I carried my pack
As far as a scout could travel.

Till I lost my boyhood and found my wife,
A girl like a Salem clipper!
A woman straight as a hunting-knife
With eyes as bright as the Dipper!

We cleared our camp where the buffalo feed,
Unheard-of streams were our flagons;
And I sowed my sons like apple-seed
On the trail of the Western wagons.

They were right, tight boys, never sulky or slow,
A fruitful, a goodly muster.
The eldest died at the Alamo.
The youngest fell with Custer.

The letter that told it burned my hand,
Yet we smiled and said, 'So be it!'
But I could not live when they fenced the land,
For it broke my heart to see it.

I saddled a red, unbroken colt
And rode him into the day there;
And he threw me down like a thunderbolt
And rolled on me as I lay there.

The hunter's whistle hummed in my ear
As the city-men tried to move me,
And I died in my boots like a pioneer
With the whole wide sky above me.

Now I lie in the heart of the fat, black soil,
Like the seed of a prairie-thistle;
It has washed my bones with honey and oil
And picked them clean as a whistle.

And my youth returns, like the rains of Spring,
And my sons, like the wild geese flying;
And I lie and hear the meadow-lark sing
And have much content in my dying.

Go play with the towns you have built of blocks,
The towns where you would have bound me!
I sleep in my earth like a tired fox,
And my buffalo have found me.

Money Musk A tune used in square dancing.

COWBOY SONG

Charles Causley

I come from Salem County
Where the silver melons grow,
Where the wheat is sweet as an angel's feet
And the zithering zephyrs blow.
I walk the blue bone-orchard
In the apple-blossom snow,
When the teasy bees take their honeyed ease
And the marmalade moon hangs low.

My Maw sleeps prone on the prairie
In a boulder eiderdown,
Where the pickled stars in their little jam-jars
Hang in a hoop to town.
I haven't seen Paw since a Sunday
In eighteen seventy-three
When he packed his snap in a bitty mess-trap
And said he'd be home by tea.

Fled is my fancy sister
All weeping like the willow,
And dead is the brother I loved like no other
Who once did share my pillow.
I fly the florid water
Where run the seven geese round,
O the townsfolk talk to see me walk
Six inches off the ground.

Across the map of midnight
I trawl the turning sky,
In my green glass the salt fleets pass
The moon her fire-float by.
The girls go gay in the valley
When the boys come down from the farm,
Don't run, my joy, from a poor cowboy,
I won't do you no harm.

The bread of my twentieth birthday
I buttered with the sun,
Though I sharpen my eyes with lovers' lies
I'll never see twenty-one.
Light is my shirt with lilies,
And lined with lead my hood,
On my face as I pass is a plate of brass,
And my suit is made of wood.

Animals

THE ICE-CART

W. W. Gibson

Perched on my city office-stool
I watched with envy, while a cool
And lucky carter handled ice....
And I was wandering in a trice,
Far from the gray and grimy heat
Of that intolerable street,
O'er sapphire berg and emerald floe,
Beneath the still, cold ruby glow
Of everlasting Polar night,
Bewildered by the queer half-light,
Until I stumbled, unawares,
Upon a creek where big white bears
Plunged headlong down with flourished heels,
And floundered after shining seals
Through shivering seas of blinding blue.
And as I watched them, ere I knew,
I'd stripped, and I was swimming, too,
Among the seal-pack, young and hale,
And thrusting on with threshing tail,
With twist and twirl and sudden leap
Through crackling ice and salty deep—
Diving and doubling with my kind,
Until, at last, we left behind
Those big white, blundering bulks of death,
And lay, at length, with panting breath
Upon a far untravelled floe,
Beneath a gentle drift of snow—
Snow drifting gentle, fine and white,
Out of the endless Polar night,
Falling and falling evermore
Upon that far untravelled shore,
Till I was buried fathoms deep
Beneath that cold, white drifting sleep—
Sleep drifting deep,
Deep drifting sleep....

The carter cracked a sudden whip:
I clutched my stool with startled grip,
Awakening to the grimy heat
Of that intolerable street.

THE TOMCAT

Don Marquis

At midnight in the alley
A tomcat comes to wail,
And he chants the hate of a million years
As he swings his snaky tail.

Malevolent, bony, brindled,
Tiger and devil and bard,
His eyes are coals from the middle of hell
And his heart is black and hard.

He twists and crouches and capers
And bares his curved sharp claws,
And he sings to the stars of the jungle nights
Ere cities were, or laws.

Beast from a world primeval,
He and his leaping clan,
When the blotched red moon leers over the roofs,
Give voice to their scorn of man.

He will lie on a rug tomorrow
And lick his silky fur,
And veil the brute in his yellow eyes,
And play he's tame, and purr.

But at midnight in the alley
He will crouch again and wail,
And beat the time for his demon's song
With the swing of his demon's tail.

COYOTE

Bret Harte

A coyote is a prairie wolf, a slinking grey animal, smaller than the true wolf. (Its name is pronounced as three syllables.)

Blown out of the prairie in twilight and dew,
Half bold and half timid, yet lazy all through;
Loth ever to leave, and yet fearful to stay,
He limps in the clearing,—an outcast in grey.

A shade on the stubble, a ghost by the wall,
Now leaping, now limping, now risking a fall,
Lop-eared and large-jointed, but ever alway
A thoroughly vagabond outcast in grey.

Here, Carlo, old fellow, he's one of your kind,—
Go seek him, and bring him in out of the wind.
What! snarling, my Carlo! So—even dogs may
A thoroughly vagabond outcast in grey.

Well, take what you will,—though it be on the sly,
Marauding or begging,—I shall not ask why;
But will call it a dole, just to help on his way
A four-footed friar in orders of grey!

THE SNARE

James Stephens

I hear a sudden cry of pain!
There is a rabbit in a snare:
Now I hear the cry again,
But I cannot tell from where.

But I cannot tell from where
He is calling out for aid;
Crying on the frightened air,
Making everything afraid.

Making everything afraid,
Wrinkling up his little face,
As he cries again for aid;
And I cannot find the place!

And I cannot find the place
Where his paw is in the snare:
Little one! Oh, little one!
I am searching everywhere.

OUT OF THE ARK

From 'The Flaming Terrapin'
by Roy Campbell

Out of the Ark's grim hold
A torrent of splendour rolled—
From the hollow resounding sides,
Flashing and glittering, came
Panthers with sparkled hides,
And tigers scribbled with flame,
And lions in grisly trains
Cascading their golden manes.
They ramped in the morning light,
And over their stripes and stars
The sun-shot lightnings, quivering bright,
Rippled in zigzag bars.
The wildebeest frisked with the gale
On the crags of a hunchback mountain;
With his heels in the clouds, he flirted his tail
Like the jet of a silvery fountain.
Frail oribi sailed with their golden-skinned
And feathery limbs laid light on the wind,
And the springbok bounced, and fluttered, and flew,
Hooped their spines on the gaunt karroo.
Gay zebras pranced and snorted aloud—
With the crackle of hail their hard hoofs pelt,
And thunder breaks from the rolling cloud
That they raise on the dusty Veldt.
O, hark how the rapids of the Congo

Are chanting their rolling strains,
And the sun-dappled herds a-skipping to the song, go
Kicking up the dust on the great, grey plains—
Tsessebe, Koodoo, Buffalo, Bongo,
With the fierce wind foaming in their manes.

THE BULL

Ralph Hodgson

In their natural state cattle inhabited grassland country or 'savan-nas' and moved about in herds. Each herd would be led by a bull. The following verses describe how such a bull is forced out of leadership and how he waits for death.

See an old unhappy bull,
Sick in soul and body both,
Slouching in the undergrowth
Of the forest beautiful.
Banished from the herd he led,
Bulls and cows a thousand head.

Cranes and gaudy parrots go
Up and down the burning sky;
Tree-top cats purr drowsily
In the dim-day green below;
And troops of monkeys, nutting some,
All disputing, go and come;

And things abominable sit
Picking offal buck or swine,
On the mess and over it
Burnished flies and beetles shine,
And spiders big as bladders lie
Under hemlocks ten foot high;

And a dotted serpent curled
Round and round and round a tree,
Yellowing its greenery,
Keeps a watch on all the world,
All the world and this old bull
In the forest beautiful.

Bravely by his fall he came:
One he led, a bull of blood
Newly come to lustihood,
Fought and put his prince to shame,
Snuffed and pawed the prostrate head,
Tameless even while it bled.

There they left him, every one,
Left him there without a lick,
Left him for the birds to pick,
Left him there for carrion,
Vilely from their bosom cast
Wisdom, worth, and love at last.

When the lion left his lair
And roared his beauty through the hills,
And the vultures pecked their quills
And flew into the middle air,
Then this prince no more to reign
Came to life and lived again.

Pity him, this fallen chief,
All his splendour, all his strength,
All his body's breadth and length
Dwindled down with shame and grief,
Half the bull he was before,
Bones and leather, nothing more.

See him standing dewlap-deep
In the rushes at the lake,
Surly, stupid, half asleep,
Waiting for his heart to break
And the birds to join the flies
Feasting at his bloodshot eyes,—

Standing with his head hung down
In a stupor, dreaming things:
Green savannas, jungles brown,
Battlefields and bellowings,
Bulls undone and lions dead
And vultures flapping overhead.

Dreaming things; of days he spent
With his mother gaunt and lean
In the valley warm and green,

Full of baby wonderment,
Blinking out of silly eyes
At a hundred mysteries;

And his little frame grew stout,
And his little legs grew strong,
And the way was not so long;
And his little horns came out,
And he played at butting trees
And boulder-stones and tortoises,

Joined a game of knobby skulls
With the youngsters of his year,
All the other little bulls,
Learning both to bruise and bear,
Learning how to stand a shock
Like a little bull of rock.

Dreaming of a day less dim,
Dreaming of a time less far,
When the faint but certain star,
Of destiny burned clear for him,
And a fierce and wild unrest
Broke the quiet of his breast.

And the gristles of his youth
Hardened in his comely pow,
And he came to fighting growth,
Beat his bull and won his cow,
And flew his tail and trampled off
Past the tallest, vain enough.

And curved about in splendour full,
And curved again and snuffed the airs,
As who should say Come out who dares!
And all beheld a bull, a bull,
And knew that here was surely one
That backed for no bull, fearing none.

Dreaming, this old bull forlorn,
Surely dreaming of the hour
When he came to sultan power,
And they owned him master-horn,
Chiefest bull of all among
Bulls and cows a thousand strong.

And in all the tramping herd
Not a bull that barred his way,
Not a cow that said him nay,
Not a bull or cow that erred
In the furnace of his look,
Dared a second, worse rebuke;

Not in all the forest wide,
Jungle, thicket, pasture, fen,
Not another dared him then,
Dared him and again defied;
Not a sovereign buck or boar
Came a second time for more.

Not a serpent that survived
Once the terrors of his hoof
Risked a second time reproof,
Came a second time and lived,
Not a serpent in its skin
Came again for discipline;

Not a leopard bright as flame,
Flashing fingerhooks of steel,
That a wooden tree might feel,
Met his fury once and came
For a second reprimand,
Not a leopard in the land.

Not a lion of them all,
Not a lion of the hills,
Hero of a thousand kills,
Dared a second fight and fall,
Dared that ram terrific twice,
Paid a second time the price. . . .

Pity him, this dupe of dream,
Leader of the herd again
Only in his daft old brain,
Once again the bull supreme
And bull enough to bear the part
Only in his tameless heart.

Pity him that he must wake;
Even now the swarm of flies
Blackening his bloodshot eyes

Bursts and blusters round the lake,
Scattered from the feast half-fed
By great shadows overhead.

And the dreamer turns away
From his visionary herds
And his splendid yesterday,
Turns to meet the loathly birds
Flocking round him from the skies,
Waiting for the flesh that dies.

IN THE DROVING DAYS

A. B. Paterson

The sight of an old horse up for auction takes the poet back to his cattle-droving days. A dingo is a native dog. The author, 'Banjo' Paterson, followed Adam Lindsay Gordon as the poet of the Australian 'outback'.

'Only a pound,' said the auctioneer,
'Only a pound; and I'm standing here
Selling this animal, gain or loss.
Only a pound for the drover's horse;
One of the sort that was never afraid,
One of the boys of the Old Brigade;
Thoroughly honest and game, I'll swear,
Only a little the worse for wear;
Plenty as bad to be seen in town,
Give me a bid and I'll knock him down;
Sold as he stands, and without recourse,
Give me a bid for the drover's horse.'

Loitering there in an aimless way
Somehow I noticed the poor old grey,
Weary and battered and screwed, of course,
Yet when I noticed the old grey horse,
The rough bush saddle, and single rein
Of the bridle laid on his tangled mane,
Straightaway the crowd and the auctioneer
Seemed on a sudden to disappear,
Melted away in a kind of haze,
For my heart went back to the droving days.

43

Back to the road, and I crossed again
Over the miles of the saltbush plain—
The shining plain that is said to be
The dried-up bed of an inland sea,
Where the air so dry and so clear and bright
Refracts the sun with a wondrous light,
And out in the dim horizon makes
The deep blue gleam of the phantom lakes.

At dawn of day we would feel the breeze
That stirred the boughs of the sleeping trees,
And brought a breath of the fragrance rare
That comes and goes in that scented air;
For the trees and grass and the shrubs contain
A dry sweet scent on the saltbush plain.
For those that love it and understand,
The saltbush is a wonderland.
A wondrous country, where Nature's ways
Were revealed to me in the droving days.

We saw the fleet wild horses pass,
And the kangaroos through the Mitchell grass,
The emu ran with her frightened brood
All unmolested and unpursued.
But there rose a shout and a wild hubbub
When the dingo raced for his native scrub,
And he paid right dear for his stolen meals
With the drover's dogs at his wretched heels.
For we ran him down at a rattling pace,
While the packhorse joined in the stirring chase.
And a wild halloo at the kill we'd raise—
We were light of heart in the droving days.

'Twas a drover's horse, and my hand again
Made a move to close on a fancied rein.
For I felt the swing and the easy stride
Of the grand old horse that I used to ride.
In drought or plenty, in good or ill,
That same old steed was my comrade still;
The old grey horse with its honest ways
Was a mate to me in the droving days.

When we kept our watch in the cold and damp,
If the cattle broke from the sleeping camp,
Over the flats and across the plain,
With my head bent down on his waving mane,
Through the boughs above and the stumps below

On the darkest night I could let him go
At a racing speed; he would choose his course,
And my life was safe with the old grey horse.
But man and horse had a favourite job,
When an outlaw broke from a station mob.
With a right good will was the stockwhip plied,
As the old horse raced at the straggler's side,
And the greenhide whip such a weal would raise—
We could use the whip in the droving days.

'Only a pound!' and was this the end—
Only a pound for the drover's friend,
The drover's friend that had seen his day,
And now was worthless, and cast away
With a broken knee and a broken heart
To be flogged and starved in a hawker's cart.
Well, I made a bid for a sense of shame
And the memories dear of the good old game.

'Thank you! Guinea! and cheap at that!
Against you there in the curly hat!
Only a guinea, and one more chance,
Down he goes if there's no advance,
Third, and the last time, one! two! three!'
And the old grey horse was knocked down to me.

And now he's wandering, fat and sleek,
On the lucerne flats by the Homestead Creek;
I dare not ride him for fear he'd fall,
But he does a journey to beat them all,
For though he scarcely a trot can raise,
He can take me back to the droving days.

AN OTTER

Ted Hughes

I

Underwater eyes, an eel's
Oil of water body, neither fish nor beast is the otter:
Four-legged yet water-gifted, to outfish fish;
With webbed feet and long ruddering tail
And a round head like an old tomcat.

45

Brings the legend of himself
From before wars or burials, in spite of hounds and vermin-
    poles;
Does not take root like the badger. Wanders, cries;
Gallops along land he no longer belongs to;
Re-enters the water by melting.

Of neither water nor land. Seeking
Some world lost when first he dived, that he cannot come at
    since,
Takes his changed body into the holes of lakes;
As if blind, cleaves the stream's push till he licks
The pebbles of the source; from sea

To sea crosses in three nights
Like a king in hiding. Crying to the old shape of the starlit
    land,
Over sunken farms where the bats go round,
Without answer. Till light and birdsong come
Walloping up roads with the milk wagon.

II

The hunt's lost him. Pads on mud,
Among sedges, nostrils a surface bead,
The otter remains, hours. The air,
Circling the globe, tainted and necessary,

Mingling tobacco-smoke, hounds and parsley,
Comes carefully to the sunk lungs.
So the self under the eye lies,
Attendant and withdrawn. The otter belongs

In double robbery and concealment—
From water that nourishes and drowns, and from land
That gave him his length and the mouth of the hound.
He keeps fat in the limpid integument

Reflections live on. The heart beats thick,
Big trout muscle out of the dead cold;
Blood is the belly of logic; he will lick
The fishbone bare. And can take stolen hold

On a bitch otter in a field full
Of nervous horses, but linger nowhere.
Yanked above hounds, reverts to nothing at all,
To this long pelt over the back of a chair.

Railways

CASEY JONES

Anonymous

This is an American ballad of modern times. Casey Jones was an engine-driver who boasted that he always brought his train in on time and who was famed for his peculiar skill with the whistle. On 30 April 1900 he was driving a train called the 'Cannon Ball Express' and ran into a stationary train. Before the collision he ordered his fireman to jump but he himself stayed on board. He succeeded in applying the brakes so that the lives of the passengers were saved but he himself was killed.

Come all you rounders if you want to hear
The story of a brave engineer;
Casey Jones was the hogger's name,
On a big eight-wheeler, boys, he won his fame.
Caller called Casey at half-past four;
He kissed his wife at the station door,
Mounted to the cabin with orders in his hand,
And took his farewell trip to the promised land.

Casey Jones, he mounted to the cabin,
Casey Jones, with his orders in his hand!
Casey Jones, he mounted to the cabin,
Took his farewell trip into the promised land.

Put in your water and shovel in your coal,
Put your head out the window, watch the drivers roll.
I'll run her till she leaves the rail,
'Cause we're eight hours late with the Western Mail!
He looked at his watch and his watch was slow,
Looked at the water and the water was low,
Turned to his fireboy and said,
'We'll get to 'Frisco, but we'll all be dead!'

Casey pulled up Reno Hill,
Tooted for the crossing with an awful shrill,
Snakes all knew by the engine's moans
That the hogger at the throttle was Casey Jones.

47

He pulled up short two miles from the place,
Number Four stared him right in the face;
Turned to his fireboy, said 'You'd better jump,
'Cause there's two locomotives that's going to bump!'

Casey said, just before he died,
'There's two more roads I'd like to ride.'
Fireboy said, 'What can they be?'
'The Rio Grand and the old S.P.'
Mrs. Jones sat on her bed a-sighing.
Got a pink that Casey was dying,
Said, 'Go to bed, children; hush your crying,
'Cause you'll get another papa on the Salt Lake line.'

Casey Jones! Got another papa!
Casey Jones, on the Salt Lake line!
Casey Jones! Got another papa!
Got another papa on the Salt Lake Line!

NIGHT MAIL

W. H. Auden

*This poem begins with a train's journey across the Border country
and down to the city of Glasgow; and goes on to describe the mail
that it was carrying.*
   The poem was written to accompany a G.P.O. publicity film.

This is the night mail crossing the border,
Bringing the cheque and the postal order,
Letters for the rich, letters for the poor,
The shop at the corner and the girl next door.
Pulling up Beattock, a steady climb—
The gradient's against her, but she's on time.

Past cotton grass and moorland boulder,
Shovelling white steam over her shoulder,
Snorting noisily as she passes
Silent miles of wind-bent grasses.
Birds turn their heads as she approaches,

Stare from the bushes at her blank-faced coaches.
Sheepdogs cannot turn her course,
They slumber on with paws across.
In the farm she passes no one wakes,
But a jug in the bedroom gently shakes.

Dawn freshens, the climb is done.
Down towards Glasgow she descends
Towards the steam tugs yelping down the glade of cranes,
Towards the fields of apparatus, the furnaces
Set on the dark plain like gigantic chessmen.
All Scotland waits for her:
In the dark glens, beside the pale-green lochs,
Men long for news.

Letters of thanks, letters from banks,
Letters of joy from girl and boy,
Receipted bills, and invitations
To inspect new stock or visit relations,
And applications for situations
And timid lovers' declarations
And gossip, gossip from all the nations,
News circumstantial, news financial,
Letters with holiday snaps to enlarge in,
Letters with faces scrawled in the margin,
Letters from uncles, cousins and aunts,
Letters to Scotland from the South of France,
Letters of condolence to Highlands and Lowlands
Notes from overseas to Hebrides
Written on paper of every hue,
The pink, the violet, the white and the blue,
The chatty, the catty, the boring, adoring,
The cold and official and the heart's outpouring,
Clever, stupid, short and long,
The typed and the printed and the spelt all wrong.

Thousands are still asleep
Dreaming of terrifying monsters,
Or a friendly tea beside the band at Cranston's or Crawford's,
Asleep in working Glasgow, asleep in well-set Edinburgh,
Asleep in granite Aberdeen.
They continue their dreams;
But shall wake soon and long for letters,
And none will hear the postman's knock
Without a quickening of the heart,
For who can hear and feel himself forgotten?

49

THE BRIDGE

J. Redwood Anderson

Here, with one leap,
The bridge that spans the cutting; on its back
The load
Of the main road
And under it the railway track.

Into the plains they sweep,
Into the solitary plains asleep,
The flowing lines, the parallel lines of steel—
Fringed with their narrow grass,
Into the plains they pass,
The flowing lines, like arms of mute appeal.

A cry
Prolonged across the earth—a call
To the remote horizon and the sky;
The whole east rushes down them with its light,
And the whole west receives them, with its pall
Of stars and night—
The flowing lines, the parallel lines of steel.

And with the fall
Of darkness, see! the red
Bright anger of the signal, where it flares
Like a huge eye that stares
On some hid danger in the dark ahead.
A twang of wire—unseen
The signal drops; and now, instead
Of a red eye, a green.

Out of the silence grows
An iron thunder—grows, and roars, and sweeps,
Menacing! The plain
Suddenly leaps,
Startled, from its repose—
Alert and listening. Now from the gloom
Of the soft distance loom
Three lights and, over them, a brush

Of tawny flame and flying spark—
Three pointed lights that rush,
Monstrous, upon the cringing dark.
And nearer, nearer rolls the sound,
Louder the throb and roar of wheels,
The shout of speed, the shriek of steam;
The sloping bank,
Cut into flashing squares, gives back the clank
And grind of metal, while the ground
Shudders and the bridge reels—
As, with a scream,
The train,
A rage of smoke, a laugh of fire,
A lighted anguish of desire,
A dream
Of gold and iron, of sound and flight,
Tumultuous roars across the night.

The train roars past—and, with a cry,
Drowned in a flying howl of wind,
Half stifled in the smoke and blind,
The plain,
Shaken, exultant, unconfined,
Rises, sweeps on, and follows, and sweeps by,
Shrieking, to lose itself in distance and the sky.

The sea

SIR HUMPHREY GILBERT

Henry Wadsworth Longfellow

*In 1583 Sir Humphrey Gilbert established the first British colony
in America at St. John's, Newfoundland. On the return voyage he
had five small ships.*

*'Munday the ninth of September in the afternoone, the Frigat
was neere cast away, oppressed by waves, yet at that time re-
covered: and giving foorth signes of joy, the Generall sitting abaft
with a booke in his hand, cried out unto us in the Hinde (so oft as
we did approach within hearing), We are as neere to heaven by
sea as by land.*

*'The same Munday night, the Frigat being ahead of us in the
Golden Hinde, suddenly her lights were out, whereof as it were in
a moment, we lost the sight, and withall our watch cryed, the
Generall was cast away, which was too true. For in that moment,
the Frigat was devoured and swallowed up of the sea.'*

Hakluyt's 'Voyages'

Southward with fleet of ice
Sailed the corsair of Death:
Wild and fast blew the blast,
And the east wind was his breath.

His lordly ships of ice
Glistened in the sun;
On each side, like pennons wide,
Flashing crystal streamlets run.

His sails of white sea-mist
Dripped with silver rain;
But where he passed there were cast
Leaden showers o'er the main.

Eastward from Campobello
Sir Humphrey Gilbert sailed;
Three days or more seaward he bore,
Then, alas, the land-wind failed.

Alas! the land-wind failed,
And ice-cold grew the night:

And never more, on sea or shore,
Should Sir Humphrey see the light.

He sat upon the deck,
The Book was in his hand;
'Do not fear! Heaven is as near'
He said, 'by water as by land!'

In the first watch of the night,
Without a signal's sound,
Out of the sea mysteriously
The fleet of Death rose all round.

The moon and evening star
Were hanging in the shrouds;
Every mast, as it passed,
Seemed to rake the passing clouds.

They grappled with their prize
At midnight black and cold!
As of a rock was the shock;
Heavily the ground-swell rolled.

Southward through day and dark
They drift in close embrace,
With mist and rain, to the open main;
Yet there seems no change of place.

Southward, for ever southward,
They drift through dark and day;
And like a dream, in the Gulf-stream
Sinking, vanish all away.

DRAKE'S DRUM

Sir Henry Newbolt

*Drake died at sea off Nombre de Dios in the West Indies in 1596.
His drum, used in those days for signalling orders to the crew, was
brought back to his home at Buckland Abbey. A legend grew up
that it would sound whenever England was in national danger.*

Drake he's in his hammock an' a thousand mile away,
(Capten, art tha sleepin' there below?),
Slung atween the round shot in Nombre Dios Bay,
An' dreamin' arl the time o' Plymouth Hoe.

Yarnder lumes the Island, yarnder lie the ships,
Wi' sailor lads a dancin' heel-an'-toe,
An' the shore-lights flashin', and the night-tide dashin',
He sees et arl so plainly as he saw et long ago.

Drake he was a Devon man, an' ruled the Devon seas,
(Capten, art tha sleepin' there below?),
Rovin' tho' his death fell, he went wi' heart at ease,
An' dreamin' arl the time o' Plymouth Hoe.
'Take my drum to England, hang et by the shore,
Strike et when your powder's runnin' low;
If the Dons sight Devon, I'll quit the port o' Heaven,
An' drum them up the Channel as we drummed them long ago.'

Drake he's in his hammock till the great Armadas come,
(Capten, art tha sleepin' there below?),
Slung atween the round shot, listenin' for the drum,
An' dreamin' arl the time o' Plymouth Hoe.
Call him on the deep sea, call him up the Sound,
Call him when ye sail to meet the foe;
Where the old trade's plyin' an' the old flag flyin'
They shall find him ware an' wakin', as they found him long
    ago!

A BALLAD TO QUEEN ELIZABETH

(Of the Spanish Armada)

Austin Dobson

King Philip had vaunted his claims;
He had sworn for a year he would sack us;
With an army of heathenish names
He was coming to fagot and stack us;
Like the thieves of the sea he would track us,
And shatter our ships on the main;
But we had bold Neptune to back us,—
And where are the galleons of Spain?

His carackes were christen'd of dames
To the kirtles whereof he would tack us;
With his saints and his gilded stern-frames,
He had thought like an egg-shell to crack us;
Now Howard may get to his Flaccus,
And Drake to his Devon again,
And Hawkins bowl rubbers to Bacchus,—
For where are the galleons of Spain?

Let his Majesty hang to St. James
The axe that he whetted to hack us;
He must play at some lustier games
Or at sea he can hope to out-thwack us;
To his mines of Peru he would pack us
To tug at his bullet and chain;
Alas that his Greatness should lack us!—
But where are the galleons of Spain?

Envoy

Gloriana!—the Don may attack us
Whenever his stomach be fain;
He must reach us before he can rack us, ...
And where are the galleons of Spain?

THE FIGHTING TÉMÉRAIRE

Sir Henry Newbolt

At Trafalgar the English fleet, led by Nelson and Collingwood, attacked in two columns almost at right angles to the line of the combined French and Spanish fleets. 'Téméraire' was immediately behind 'Victory'.
   W. J. Turner painted a famous picture entitled 'The Fighting Téméraire Tugged to her Last Berth to be Broken Up'.

It was eight bells ringing,
For the morning watch was done,
And the gunner's lads were singing
As they polished every gun.
It was eight bells ringing,
And the gunner's lads were singing,
For the ship she rode a-swinging
As they polished every gun.

Oh! to see the linstock lighting,
Téméraire! Téméraire!
Oh! to hear the round shot biting,
Téméraire! Téméraire!
Oh! to see the linstock lighting,
And to hear the round shot biting,
For we're all in love with fighting
On the Fighting Téméraire.

It was noontide ringing,
And the battle just begun,
When the ship her way was winging
As they loaded every gun.
It was noontide ringing,
When the ship her way was winging,
And the gunner's lads were singing
As they loaded every gun.

There'll be many grim and gory,
Téméraire! Téméraire!
There'll be few to tell the story,
Téméraire! Téméraire!
There'll be many grim and gory,
There'll be few to tell the story,
But we'll all be one in glory
With the Fighting Téméraire.

There's a far bell ringing
At the setting of the sun,
And a phantom voice is singing
Of the great days done.
There's a far bell ringing,
And a phantom voice is singing
Of renown for ever clinging
To the great days done.

Now the sunset breezes shiver,
Téméraire! Téméraire!
And she's fading down the river,
Téméraire! Téméraire!
Now the sunset breezes shiver,
And she's fading down the river,
But in England's song for ever
She's the Fighting Téméraire.

SKIPPER IRESON'S RIDE

John Greenleaf Whittier

*Whittier wrote this poem from a fragment of rhyme remembered
from boyhood. It tells the story of a New England fishing-captain,
Floyd Ireson, who was tarred and feathered by the women of
Marblehead for refusing to go to the rescue of a leaking ship.*

*According to the poem he did so 'for his hard heart'; Whittier
did not learn until later the truth of the incident, that Ireson
received unjust blame for the action of a stubborn and cowardly
crew.*

Of all the rides since the birth of time,
Told in story or sung in rhyme,—
On Apuleius's Golden Ass,
Or one-eyed Calendar's horse of brass,
Witch astride of a human back,
Islam's prophet on Al-Borak,—
The strangest ride that ever was sped
Was Ireson's, out from Marblehead!
Old Floyd Ireson, for his hard heart,
Tarred and feathered and carried in a cart
By the women of Marblehead!

Body of turkey, head of owl,
Wings a-droop like a rained-on fowl,
Feathered and ruffled in every part,
Skipper Ireson stood in the cart.
Scores of women, old and young,
Strong of muscle, and glib of tongue,
Pushed and pulled up the rocky lane,
Shouting and singing the shrill refrain:
'Here's Flud Oirson, fur his horrd horrt,
Torr'd an' furtherr'd an' corr'd in a corrt
By the women o' Morble'ead!'

Wrinkled scolds with hands on hips,
Girls in bloom of cheek and lips,
Wild-eyed, free-limbed, such as chase
Bacchus round some antique vase,
Brief of skirt, with ankles bare,
Loose of kerchief and loose of hair,
With conch-shells blowing and fish-horns' twang,
Over and over the Mænads sang:

'Here's Flud Oirson, fur his horrd horrt,
Torr'd an' futher'd an' corr'd in a corrt
By the women o' Morble'ead!'

Small pity for him!—He sailed away
From a leaking ship, in Chaleur Bay,—
Sailed away from a sinking wreck,
With his own town's-people on her deck!
'Lay by! lay by!' they called to him.
Back he answered, 'Sink or swim!
Brag of your catch of fish again!'
And off he sailed through the fog and rain,
Old Floyd Ireson, for his hard heart,
Tarred and feathered and carried in a cart
By the women of Marblehead!

Fathoms deep in dark Chaleur
That wreck shall lie for evermore.
Mother and sister, wife and maid,
Looked from the rocks of Marblehead
Over the moaning and rainy sea,—
Looked for the coming that might not be!
What did the winds and the sea-birds say
Of the cruel captain who sailed away?—
Old Floyd Ireson, for his hard heart,
Tarred and feathered and carried in a cart
By the women of Marblehead!

Through the street, on either side,
Up flew windows, doors swung wide;
Sharp-tongued spinsters, old wives grey,
Treble lent the fish-horn's bray.
Sea-worn grandsires, cripple-bound,
Hulks of old sailors run aground,
Shook head, and fist, and hat, and cane,
And cracked with curses the hoarse refrain:
'Here's Flud Oirson, fur his horrd horrt,
Torr'd an' furtherr'd an' corr'd in a corrt
By the women o' Morble'ead!'

Sweetly along the Salem road
Bloom of orchard and lilac showed.
Little the wicked skipper knew
Of the fields so green and the sky so blue.
Riding there in his sorry trim,

Like an Indian idol glum and grim,
Scarcely he seemed the sound to hear
Of voices shouting, far and near:
'Here's Flud Oirson, fur his horrd horrt,
Torr'd an' furtherr'd an' corr'd in a corrt
By the women o' Morble'ead!'

'Hear me, neighbours!' at last he cried,—
'What to me is this noisy ride?
What is the shame that clothes the skin
To the nameless horror that lives within?
Waking or sleeping, I see a wreck,
And hear a cry from a reeling deck!
Hate me and curse me,—I only dread
The hand of God and the face of the dead!'
Said old Floyd Ireson, for his hard heart,
Tarred and feathered and carried in a cart
By the women of Marblehead!

Then the wife of the skipper lost at sea
Said, 'God has touched him! Why should we?'
Said an old wife, mourning her only son:
'Cut the rogue's tether and let him run!'
So with soft relentings and rude excuse,
Half scorn, half pity, they cut him loose,
And gave him a cloak to hide him in,
And left him alone with his shame and sin.
Poor Floyd Ireson, for his hard heart,
Tarred and feathered and carried in a cart
By the women of Marblehead!

Warfare

THE DESTRUCTION OF SENNACHERIB

Lord Byron

At one period in Old Testament history, Israel was dominated by the kingdom of Assyria, ruled by Sennacherib from the city of Nineveh. The Assyrians were idolaters, worshipping Baal and other gods.

Byron's imagination was stirred by the following verse from 2 Kings xix: 'And it came to pass that night, that the angel of the Lord went out, and smote in the camp of the Assyrians an hundred fourscore and five thousand: and when they arose early in the morning, behold, they were all dead corpses.'

The Assyrian came down like the wolf on the fold,
And his cohorts were gleaming in purple and gold;
And the sheen of their spears was like stars on the sea,
When the blue wave rolls nightly on deep Galilee.

Like the leaves of the forest when summer is green,
That host with their banners at sunset were seen :
Like the leaves of the forest when autumn hath blown,
That host on the morrow lay withered and strown.

For the Angel of Death spread his wings on the blast,
And breathed on the face of the foe as he passed :
And the eyes of the sleepers waxed deadly and chill,
And their hearts but once heaved, and for ever grew still!

And there lay the steed with his nostril all wide,
And through it there rolled not the breath of his pride :
And the foam of his gasping lay white on the turf,
And cold as the spray of the rock-beating surf.

And there lay the rider, distorted and pale,
With the dew on his brow and the rust on his mail;
The tents were all silent, the banners alone,
The lances unlifted, the trumpet unblown.

And the widows of Asshur are loud in their wail,
And the idols are broke in the temple of Baal;
And the might of the Gentile, unsmote by the sword,
Hath melted like snow in the glance of the Lord!

THE WAR SONG OF DINAS VAWR

Thomas Love Peacock

The mountain sheep are sweeter,
But the valley sheep are fatter;
We therefore deemed it meeter
To carry off the latter.
We made an expedition;
We met a host and quelled it;
We forced a strong position,
And killed the men who held it.

On Dyfed's richest valley,
Where herds of kine were browsing,
We made a mighty sally,
To furnish our carousing.
Fierce warriors rushed to meet us;
We met them, and o'erthrew them;
They struggled hard to beat us;
But we conquered them, and slew them.

As we drove our prize at leisure,
The king marched forth to catch us:
His rage surpassed all measure,
But his people could not match us.
He fled to his hall-pillars;
And, ere our force we led off,
Some sacked his house and cellars,
While others cut his head off.

We there, in strife bewildering,
Spilt blood enough to swim in:
We orphaned many children,
And widowed many women.

The eagles and the ravens
We glutted with our foemen;
The heroes and the cravens,
The spearmen and the bowmen.

We brought away from battle,
And much their land bemoaned them,
Two thousand head of cattle,
And the head of him who owned them:
Ednyfed, King of Dyfed,
His head was borne before us;
His wine and beasts supplied our feasts,
And his overthrow, our chorus.

GATHERING SONG OF DONALD THE BLACK

Sir Walter Scott

*This poem, known also as the 'Pibroch of Donuil Dhu', is linked
with Clan McDonald and refers to an incident of the fifteenth
century. Donald Balloch invaded Lochaber with a strong force
from the Isles and defeated the Earls of Mar and Caithness at
Inverlochy.*

Pibroch of Donuil Dhu,
Pibroch of Donuil,
Wake thy wild voice anew,
Summon Clan Conuil.
Come away, come away,
Hark to the summons!
Come in your war array,
Gentles and commons.

Come from deep glen, and
From mountain so rocky,
The war-pipe and pennon
Are at Inverlochy.
Come every hill-plaid, and
True heart that wears one,
Come every steel blade, and
Strong hand that bears one.

Leave untended the herd,
The flock without shelter;
Leave the corpse uninterr'd,
The bride at the altar;

Leave the deer, leave the steer,
Leave nets and barges;
Come with your fighting gear,
Broadswords and targes.

Come as the winds come, when
Forests are rended,
Come as the waves come, when
Navies are stranded :
Faster come, faster come,
Faster and faster,
Chief, vassal, page and groom,
Tenant and master.

Fast they come, fast they come;
See how they gather!
Wide waves the eagle plume,
Blended with heather.
Cast your plaids, draw your blades,
Forward each man set!
Pibroch of Donuil Dhu,
Knell for the onset!

HENRY V BEFORE THE BATTLE OF AGINCOURT

William Shakespeare

Shakespeare's play, 'King Henry the Fifth', deals with an invasion of France by the English, culminating in the Battle of Agincourt at which the English were very much outnumbered by the French.
Just before battle is joined, one of his nobles suggests to Henry that they could well do with the help of men who had remained in England. Henry scorns the suggestion—'the fewer men, the greater share of honour', he says.

This day is called the feast of Crispian.
He that outlives this day, and comes safe home,
Will stand a tip-toe when this day is named,
And rouse him at the name of Crispian.
He that shall live this day, and see old age,
Will yearly on the vigil feast his neighbours,
And say, 'To-morrow is Saint Crispian.'
Then will he strip his sleeve and show his scars,
And say, 'These wounds I had on Crispin's day.'
Old men forget; yet all shall be forgot,

But he'll remember, with advantages,
What feats he did that day. Then shall our names,
Familiar in his mouth as household words—
Harry the king, Bedford and Exeter,
Warwick and Talbot, Salisbury and Gloucester—
Be in their flowing cups freshly remembered.
This story shall the good man teach his son;
An Crispin Crispian shall ne'er go by,
From this day to the ending of the world,
But we in it shall be remembered—
We few, we happy few, we band of brothers;
For he to-day that sheds his blood with me
Shall be my brother; be he ne'er so vile,
This day shall gentle his condition;
And gentlemen in England now a-bed
Shall think themselves accursed they were not here,
And hold their manhoods cheap while any speaks,
That fought with us upon Saint Crispin's day.

HOHENLINDEN

Thomas Campbell

*At Hohenlinden in Bavaria the French revolutionary army defeated
the Austrians in 1800.*

On Linden, when the sun was low,
All bloodless lay the untrodden snow,
And dark as winter was the flow
Of Iser, rolling rapidly.

But Linden saw another sight,
When the drum beat, at dead of night,
Commanding fires of death to light
The darkness of her scenery.

By torch and trumpet fast arrayed,
Each horseman drew his battle blade,
And furious every charger neighed,
To join the dreadful revelry.

Then shook the hills with thunder riven,
Then rushed the steed to battle driven,
And louder than the bolts of heaven,
Far flashed the red artillery.

But redder yet that light shall glow
On Linden's hills of stainéd snow,
And bloodier yet the torrent flow
Of Iser rolling rapidly.

'Tis morn, but scarce yon level sun
Can pierce the war-clouds, rolling dun,
Where furious Frank and fiery Hun
Shout in their sulph'rous canopy.

The combat deepens. On, ye brave,
Who rush to glory, or the grave!
Wave, Munich! all thy banners wave,
And charge with all thy chivalry!

Few, few, shall part where many meet!
The snow shall be their winding-sheet,
And every turf beneath their feet
Shall be a soldier's sepulchre.

THE BURIAL OF SIR JOHN MOORE AT CORUNNA

Charles Wolfe

In 1809 the French armies of Napoleon held Spain. An English army under Moore was landed to assist the Spaniards in revolt but it was outnumbered and forced to retreat on the port of Corunna. The army was embarked on the transports but Moore lost his life in a rearguard engagement.

Not a drum was heard, not a funeral note,
As his corse to the rampart we hurried;
Not a soldier discharged his farewell shot
O'er the grave where our hero we buried.

We buried him darkly at dead of night,
The sods with our bayonets turning;
By the struggling moonbeam's misty light
And the lantern dimly burning.

No useless coffin enclosed his breast,
Not in sheet or in shroud we wound him;
But he lay like a warrior taking his rest,
With his martial cloak around him.

Few and short were the prayers we said,
And we spoke not a word of sorrow;
But we steadfastly gazed on the face that was dead,
And we bitterly thought of the morrow.

We thought, as we hollow'd his narrow bed
And smoothed down his lonely pillow,
That the foe and the stranger would tread o'er his head
And we far away on the billow!

Lightly they'll talk of the spirit that's gone
And o'er his cold ashes upbraid him,—
But little he'll reck, if they let him sleep on
In the grave where a Briton has laid him.

But half of our heavy task was done
When the clock struck the hour for retiring,
And we heard the distant and random gun
That the foe was sullenly firing.

Slowly and sadly we laid him down,
From the field of his fame fresh and gory;
We carved not a line, and we raised not a stone,
But we left him alone with his glory.

PICARDIE

Alys Fane Trotter

*This poem was written by the mother of a young man, Lieutenant
A. N. Trotter, who was killed near Béthune in France early in the
First World War. In it she recalled a holiday they had spent as a
family in the same district six years earlier when her son was a boy
of fourteen.*

There's a pathway through the forest in the Picardie I know,
A port where girls haul up the boats with men and fish in tow,
And the hills run down to the market town where the country-
      women go.

And behind it is the village, and the coast-line lies below,
And down the road, the dusty road, the carts ply to and fro
By the stately frieze of forest trees beyond the old Chateau.

There were three of us on bicycles upon the road that day;
You wore your coat of hunting green, and vanished down the
    way.
'Le petit Chasseur, la mère et sœur,' we heard the women say.

You vanished as a speck of green among the shadows blue,
And children trudging up the hill stood still and called to you :
'Le petit Chasseur, qui n'a pas peur,' they laughed and called to
    you.

O boys, you wield the bayonet now and lift the soldier's load!
O girls, you've learnt to drive the plough and use the bullock-
    goad!
But the hunter's laid, still unafraid, near the trodden Béthune
    road.

There's a pathway through the forest in the Picardie I know,
And O I'll dream and wander there; and poppy fields will glow;
And I'll watch the glare of the dusty air where the market
    wagons go.

MINE-SWEEPING TRAWLERS

E. Hilton Young

Not ours the fighter's glow,
The glory and the praise;
Unnoticed to and fro
We pass our dangerous ways.

We sift the drifting sea
And blindly grope beneath;
Obscure and toilsome we,
The fishermen of death.

But when the great ships go
To battle through the gloom,
Our hearts beat high to know
We cleared their path of doom.

NAMING OF PARTS

Henry Reed

To-day we have naming of parts. Yesterday,
We had daily cleaning. And to-morrow morning,
We shall have what to do after firing. But to-day,
To-day we have naming of parts. Japonica
Glistens like coral in all of the neighbouring gardens,
And to-day we have naming of parts.

This is the lower sling swivel. And this
Is the upper sling swivel, whose use you will see,
When you are given your slings. And this is the piling swivel,
Which in your case you have not got. The branches
Hold in the gardens their silent, eloquent gestures,
Which in our case we have not got.

This is the safety-catch, which is always released
With an easy flick of the thumb. And please do not let me
See anyone using his finger. You can do it quite easy
If you have any strength in your thumb. The blossoms
Are fragile and motionless, never letting anyone see
Any of them using their finger.

And this you can see is the bolt. The purpose of this
Is to open the breech, as you see. We can slide it
Rapidly backwards and forwards: we call this
Easing the spring. And rapidly backwards and forwards
The early bees are assaulting and fumbling the flowers:
They call it easing the Spring.

They call it easing the spring: it is perfectly easy
If you have any strength in your thumb: like the bolt,
And the breech, and the cocking-piece, and the point of balance,

Which in our case we have not got; and the almond-blossom
Silent in all of the gardens and the bees going backwards and
    forwards,
For to-day we have naming of parts.

HIGH FLIGHT

John Gillespie Magee

*A nineteen-year-old American fighter pilot wrote these verses on
the back of a letter to his parents. Shortly afterwards he was killed
on active service in England.*

Oh, I have slipped the surly bonds of earth,
And danced the skies on laughter-silvered wings;
Sunward I've climbed and joined the tumbling mirth
Of sun-split clouds—and done a hundred things
You have not dreamed of—wheeled and soared and swung
High in the sunlit silence. Hov'ring there,
I've chased the shouting wind along and flung
My eager craft through footless halls of air.
Up, up the long delirious burning blue
I've topped the wind-swept heights with easy grace,
Where never lark, or even eagle, flew;
And, while with silent, lifting mind I've trod
The high untrespassed sanctity of space,
Put out my hand, and touched the face of God.

NIGHT BOMBERS

Anonymous

Eastward they climb, black shapes against the grey
Of falling dusk, gone with the nodding day
From English fields. Not theirs the sudden glow
Of triumph that their fighter-brothers know;
Only to fly through cloud, through storm, through night,
Unerring, and to keep their purpose bright,
Nor turn until, their dreadful duty done,
Westward they climb to race the awakened sun.

DEATH OF AN AIRCRAFT

Charles Causley

An incident of the Cretan campaign, 1941
(*to George Psychoundakis*)

One day on our village in the month of July
An aeroplane sank from the sea of the sky,
White as a whale it smashed on the shore
Bleeding oil and petrol all over the floor.

The Germans advanced in the vertical heat
To save the dead plane from the people of Crete,
And round the glass wreck in a circus of snow
Set seven mechanical sentries to go.

Seven stalking spiders about the sharp sun
Clicking like clockwork and each with a gun
But at *Come to the Cookhouse* they wheeled about
And sat down to sausages and sauerkraut.

Down from the mountain burning so brown
Wriggled three heroes from Kastelo town,
Deep in the sand they silently sank
And each struck a match for a petrol-tank.

Up went the plane in a feather of fire
As the bubbling boys began to retire
And, grey in the guardhouse, seven Berliners
Lost their stripes as well as their dinners.

Down in the village, at murder-stations,
The Germans fell in friends and relations :
But not a Kastelian snapped an eye
As he spat in the air and prepared to die.

Not a Kastelian whispered a word
Dressed with the dust to be massacred,
And squinted up at the sky with a frown
As three bubbly boys came walking down.

One was sent to the county gaol
Too young for bullets if not for bail,
But the other two were in prime condition
To take on a load of ammunition.

In Archonti they stood in the weather
Naked, hungry, chained together:
Stark as the stones in the market-place,
Under the eyes of the populace.

Their irons unlocked as their naked hearts
They faced the squad and their funeral-carts.
The Captain cried, 'Before you're away
Is there any last word you'd like to say?'

'I want no words,' said one, 'with my lead,
Only some water to cool my head.'
'Water,' the other said, ''s all very fine
But I'll be taking a glass of wine.

A glass of wine for the afternoon
With permission to sing a signature-tune!'
And he ran the *raki* down his throat
And took a deep breath for the leading note.

But before the squad could shoot or say
Like the impala he leapt away
Over the rifles, under the biers,
The bullets rattling round his ears.

'Run!' they cried to the boy of stone
Who now stood there in the street alone,
But 'Rather than bring revenge on your head
It is better for me to die,' he said.

The soldiers turned their machine-guns round
And shot him down with a dreadful sound
Scrubbed his face with perpetual dark
And rubbed it out like a pencil mark.

But his comrade slept in the olive tree
And sailed by night on the gnawing sea,
The soldier's silver shilling earned
And, armed like an archangel, returned.

Age and death

ABRAHAM LINCOLN WALKS AT MIDNIGHT

Vachel Lindsay

Abraham Lincoln was President of the United States of America at the time of the American Civil War. The note of introduction to the poem about his mother, Nancy Hanks, on page 27, tells you something about him.

It is portentous and a thing of state
That here at midnight, in our little town,
A mourning figure walks, and will not rest,
Near the old court-house pacing up and down.

Or by his homestead, or in shadowed yards,
He lingers where his children used to play,
Or through the market, on the well-worn stones,
He stalks until the dawn-stars burn away.

A bronzed, lank man! His suit of ancient black,
A famous high-top hat and plain worn shawl
Make him the quaint great figure that men love,
The prairie lawyer, master of us all.

He cannot sleep upon his hillside now.
He is among us :—as in times before!
And we who toss and lie awake for long
Breathe deep, and start, to see him pass the door.

His head is bowed. He thinks on men and kings.
Yea, when the sick world cries, how can he sleep?
Too many peasants fight, they know not why,
Too many homesteads in black terror weep.

The sins of all the war-lords burn his heart.
He sees the dreadnoughts scouring every main.
He carries on his shawl-wrapped shoulders now
The bitterness, the folly and the pain.

He cannot rest until a spirit-dawn
Shall come :—the shining hope of Europe free :
The league of sober folk, the Worker's Earth,
Bringing long peace to Cornland, Alp and Sea.

It breaks his heart that kings must murder still,
That all his hours of travail here for men
Seem yet in vain. And who will bring white peace
That he may sleep upon his hill again?

GENERAL WILLIAM BOOTH ENTERS INTO HEAVEN

Vachel Lindsay

*William Booth founded the Salvation Army in 1878, its organiza-
tion being modelled on that of the British army. His Christian faith
was coupled with profound pity for the outcast and with a hatred
for the squalor and suffering characteristic of nineteenth-century
slums. He died in 1912.*

Booth led boldly with his big bass drum.
(Are you washed in the blood of the Lamb?)
The Saints smiled gravely and they said : 'He's come.'
(Are you washed in the blood of the Lamb?)
Walking lepers following, rank on rank,
Lurching bravos from the ditches dank,
Drabs from the alleyways and drug fiends pale—
Minds still passion-ridden, soul-powers frail :
Vermin-eaten saints with mouldy breath,
Unwashed legions with the ways of Death—
(Are you washed in the blood of the Lamb?)

Every slum had sent its half-a-score
The round world over. (Booth had groaned for more.)
Every banner that the wide world flies
Bloomed with glory and transcendent dyes.
Big-voiced lasses made their banjos bang,
Tranced, fanatical, they shrieked and sang :

'Are you washed in the blood of the Lamb?'
Hallelujah! It was queer to see
Bull-necked convicts with that land make free.
Loons with trumpets blowed a blare, blare
On, on upward thro' the golden air!
(Are you washed in the blood of the Lamb?)

Booth died blind and still by faith he trod,
Eyes still dazzled by the ways of God.
Booth led boldly, and he looked the chief,
Eagle countenance in sharp relief,
Beard a-flying, air of high command
Unabated in that holy land.

Jesus came from out the court-house door,
Stretched his hands above the passing poor.
Booth saw not, but led his queer ones there
Round and round the mighty court-house square.
Then, in an instant all that blear review
Marched on spotless, clad in raiment new.
The lame were straightened, withered limbs uncurled
And blind eyes opened on a new, sweet world.

Drabs and vixens in a flash made whole!
Gone was the weasel-head, the snout, the jowl!
Sages and sibyls now, and athletes clean,
Rulers of empires, and of forests green!
The hosts were sandalled, and their wings were fire!
(Are you washed in the blood of the Lamb?)
But their noise played havoc with the angel-choir.
(Are you washed in the blood of the Lamb?)

Oh, shout Salvation! It was good to see
Kings and Princes by the Lamb set free.
The banjos rattled and the tambourines
Jing-jing-jingled in the hands of Queens.

And when Booth halted by the curb for prayer
He saw his Master thro' the flag-filled air.
Christ came gently with a robe and crown
For Booth the soldier, while the throng knelt down.
He saw King Jesus. They were face to face,
And he knelt a-weeping in the holy place.
(Are you washed in the blood of the Lamb?)

OVER THE SEA TO SKYE

Robert Louis Stevenson

Stevenson remembers boyhood days when he sailed among the Western Isles of Scotland, days that seemed far away in space and time from his later years in Samoa. The last lines of the poem are not true, for he maintained his gallant spirit, his kindliness and courage, to the end of his life.

Sing me a song of a lad that is gone,
Say, could that lad be I!
Merry of soul he sailed on a day
Over the sea to Skye.

Mull was astern, Rum on the port,
Eigg on the starboard bow.
Glory of youth glowed in his soul;
Where is that glory now?

Sing me a song of a lad that is gone,
Say, could that lad be I?
Merry of soul he sailed on a day
Over the sea to Skye.

Give me again all that was there,
Give me the sun that shone!
Give me the eyes, give me the soul,
Give me the lad that's gone!

Sing me a song of a lad that is gone,
Say, could that lad be I?
Merry of soul he sailed on a day
Over the sea to Skye.

Billow and breeze, islands and seas,
Mountains of rain and sun,
All that was good, all that was fair,
All that was me is gone.

DIRGE

William Shakespeare

Fear no more the heat o' the sun,
Nor the furious winter's rages;
Thou thy worldly task hast done,
Home art gone and ta'en thy wages :
Golden lads and girls all must,
As chimney-sweepers, come to dust.

Fear no more the frown o' the great,
Thou art past the tyrant's stroke;
Care no more to clothe and eat;
To thee the reed is as the oak :
The sceptre, learning, physic, must
All follow this, and come to dust.

Fear no more the lightning flash
Nor the all-dreaded thunder-stone;
Fear not slander, censure rash;
Thou hast finished joy and moan :
All lovers young, all lovers must
Consign to thee, and come to dust.

TO AN ATHLETE DYING YOUNG

A. E. Housman

The time you won your town the race
We chaired you through the market place;
Man and boy stood cheering by,
And home we brought you shoulder-high.

To-day, the road all runners come,
Shoulder-high we bring you home,
And set you at your threshold down,
Townsman of a stiller town.

Smart lad, to slip betimes away
From fields where glory does not stay
And early though the laurel grows
It withers quicker than the rose.

Eyes the shady night has shut
Cannot see the record cut,
And silence sounds no worse than cheers
After earth has stopped the ears:

Now you will not swell the rout
Of lads that wore their honours out,
Runners whom renown outran
And the name died before the man.

So set, before its echoes fade,
The fleet foot on the sill of shade,
And hold to the low lintel up
The still-defended challenge-cup.

And round that early-laurelled head
Will flock to gaze the strengthless dead,
And find unwithered on its curls
The garland briefer than a girl's.

WITH RUE MY HEART IS LADEN

A. E. Housman

With rue my heart is laden
For golden friends I had,
For many a rose-lipt maiden
And many a lightfoot lad.

By brooks too broad for leaping
The lightfoot boys are laid;
The rose-lipt girls are sleeping
In fields where roses fade.

REQUIEM

Robert Louis Stevenson

This epitaph is inscribed on the poet's tomb on a hill-top in Samoa.

Under the wide and starry sky
Dig the grave and let me lie.
Glad did I live and gladly die,
And I laid me down with a will.

This be the verse you grave for me:
Here he lies where he longed to be;
Home is the sailor, home from sea,
And the hunter home from the hill.

MID-TERM BREAK

Seamus Heaney

I sat all morning in the college sick bay
Counting bells knelling classes to a close.
At two o'clock our neighbours drove me home.

In the porch I met my father crying—
He had always taken funerals in his stride—
And Big Jim Evans saying it was a hard blow.

The baby cooed and laughed and rocked the pram
When I came in, and I was embarrassed
By old men standing up to shake my hand

And tell me they were 'sorry for my trouble'.
At ten o'clock an ambulance arrived
With the corpse, stanched and bandaged by nurses.

Next morning I went up into the room. Snowdrops
And candles soothed the bedside; I saw him
For the first time in six weeks. Paler now,

Wearing a poppy bruise on his left temple,
He lay in the four-foot box as in his cot.
No gaudy scars, the bumper knocked him clear.

A four-foot box, a foot for every year.

'OUT, OUT –'*

Robert Frost

The buzz saw snarled and rattled in the yard
And made dust and dropped stove-length sticks of wood
Sweet-scented stuff when the breeze drew across it.
And from there those that lifted eyes could count
Five mountain ranges one behind the other
Under the sunset far into Vermont.
And the saw snarled and rattled, snarled and rattled,
As it ran light, or had to bear a load.
And nothing happened: day was all but done.
Call it a day, I wish they might have said
To please the boy by giving him the half hour
That a boy counts so much when saved from work.
His sister stood beside them in her apron
To tell them 'Supper'. At the word, the saw,
As if to prove saws knew what supper meant,
Leaped out at the boy's hand, or seemed to leap—
He must have given the hand. However it was,
Neither refused the meeting. But the hand!
The boy's first outcry was a rueful laugh,
As he swung toward them holding up his hand
Half in appeal, but half as if to keep
The life from spilling. Then the boy saw all—
Since he was old enough to know, big boy
Doing a man's work, though a child at heart—
He saw all spoiled. 'Don't let him cut my hand off—
The doctor, when he comes. Don't let him, sister!'
So. But the hand was gone already.
The doctor put him in the dark of ether.

---

* The title refers to a line in Shakespeare's *Macbeth*—'Out, out,
brief candle! Life's but a walking shadow ...'

He lay and puffed his lips out with his breath.
And then—the watcher at his pulse took fright.
No one believed. They listened to his heart.
Little—less—nothing! and that ended it.
No more to build on there. And they, since they
Were not the one dead, turned to their affairs.

AT 30,000 FEET

Bernard Gilhooly

A fleck of silver against the darkening blue
The hollow cylinder rockets under the sky's dome,
Unavailingly pursued by the thunder of its sound
Until that final scarlet reverberation;
Like the telegraphed words burning meaninglessly
Upon the slip of yellow paper, and the explosion
Of grief within the mind, this fire and thunder
Do not quite coincide:
The eyes of the watcher see the disaster
Before its voice awakens in his ear.

Nothing that has meaning descends again to earth;
The lighted runway waits vainly
To feel the screeching tyres;
Customs officials will not search this baggage
That downward flakes in dust on silent fields;
Hands cannot clasp, nor lips press
What is now blown weightlessly about the sky.

There was a moment when they drowsed
Deep in luxurious chairs;
Read magazines, wrote letters;
When stewardesses served coffee and liqueurs,
And dirty dishes were neatly stacked
In the bright kitchen.

No other moment followed;
Time stopped. There was nothing ...

No doubt there is a meaning to this event;
But not the one that can be read
On the white face of the farmer
In mid-furrow gazing upward from his plough,
Nor in the burned minds of those who wait
At the airport barrier.

Longer story poems

HIAWATHA'S SAILING

Henry Wadsworth Longfellow

*The American Indians had a legendary chief named Hiawatha,
supposedly a Mohawk chief of several hundred years ago.*

*Longfellow's poem reproduces a series of Indian stories centred
upon a Hiawatha who was the son of the beautiful Wenonah and
the West Wind, and who wedded Minnehaha the Dacota maiden.*

*The poem is in sections, of which 'Hiawatha's Sailing' is one.
Some of the other sections describe his childhood, his friends, his
fishing and his wooing; they deal also with the Indian picture
writing, with a season of famine and with the coming of the white
man.*

Give me of your bark, O Birch-Tree!
Of your yellow bark, O Birch-Tree!
Growing by the rushing river,
Tall and stately in the valley!
I a light canoe will build me,
Build a swift Cheemaun for sailing,
That shall float upon the river,
Like a yellow leaf in Autumn,
Like a yellow water-lily!
　'Lay aside your cloak, O Birch-Tree!
Lay aside your white-skin wrapper,
For the Summer-time is coming,
And the sun is warm in heaven,
And you need no white-skin wrapper!'
　Thus aloud cried Hiawatha
In the solitary forest,
By the rushing Taquamenaw,
When the birds were singing gaily,
In the Moon of Leaves were singing,
And the sun, from sleep awaking,
Started up and said, 'Behold me!
Gheezis, the great Sun, behold me!'
　And the tree with all its branches
Rustled in the breeze of morning,
Saying, with a sigh of patience,
'Take my cloak, O Hiawatha!'

With his knife the tree he girdled;
Just beneath its lowest branches,
Just above the roots he cut it,
Till the sap came oozing outward;
Down the trunk, from top to bottom,
Sheer he cleft the bark asunder,
With a wooden wedge he raised it,
Stripped it from the trunk unbroken.
  'Give me of your boughs, O Cedar!
Of your strong and pliant branches,
My canoe to make more steady,
Make more strong and firm beneath me!'
  Through the summit of the cedar
Went a sound, a cry of horror,
Went a murmur of resistance;
But it whispered, bending downward,
'Take my boughs, O Hiawatha!'
  Down he hewed the boughs of cedar,
Shaped them straightway to a framework,
Like two bows he formed and shaped them,
Like two bended bows together.
  'Give me of your roots, O Tamarack!
Of your fibrous roots, O Larch-Tree!
My canoe to bind together,
So to bind the ends together
That the water may not enter,
That the river may not wet me!'
  And the larch with all its fibres,
Shivered in the air of morning,
Touched his forehead with its tassels,
Said, with one long sigh of sorrow,
'Take them all, O Hiawatha!'
  From the earth he tore the fibres,
Tore the tough roots of the Larch-Tree,
Closely sewed the bark together,
Bound it closely to the framework.
  'Give me of your balm, O Fir-Tree!
Of your balsam and your resin,
So to close the seams together
That the water may not enter,
That the river may not wet me!'
  And the Fir-Tree, tall and sombre,
Sobbed through all its robes of darkness,
Rattled like a shore with pebbles,
Answered wailing, answered weeping,
'Take my balm, O Hiawatha!'

And he took the tears of balsam,
Took the resin of the Fir-Tree,
Smeared therewith each seam and fissure,
Made each crevice safe from water.

'Give me of your quills, O Hedgehog!
All your quills, O Kagh, the Hedgehog!
I will make a necklace of them,
Make a girdle for my beauty,
And two stars to deck her bosom!'

From a hollow tree the Hedgehog
With his sleepy eyes looked at him,
Shot his shining quills, like arrows,
Saying, with a drowsy murmur,
Through the tangle of his whiskers,
'Take my quills, O Hiawatha!'

From the ground the quills he gathered,
All the little shining arrows,
Stained them red and blue and yellow,
With the juice of roots and berries;
Into his canoe he wrought them,
Round its waist a shining girdle,
Round its bow a gleaming necklace,
On its breast two stars resplendent.

Thus the Birch Canoe was builded
In the valley, by the river,
In the bosom of the forest;
And the forest's life was in it,
All its mystery and its magic,
All the lightness of the birch-tree,
All the toughness of the cedar,
All the larch's supple sinews;
And it floated on the river
Like a yellow leaf in Autumn,
Like a yellow water-lily.

Paddles none had Hiawatha,
Paddles none he had or needed,
For his thoughts as paddles served him,
And his wishes served to guide him.
Swift or slow at will he glided,
Veered to right or left at pleasure.

Then he called aloud to Kwasind,
To his friend, the strong man Kwasind,
Saying, 'Help me clear this river
Of its sunken logs and sand-bars.'

Straight into the river Kwasind
Plunged as if he were an otter,

Dived as if he were a beaver,
Stood up to his waist in water,
To his armpits in the river,
Swam and shouted in the river,
Tugged at sunken logs and branches,
With his hands he scooped the sand-bars,
With his feet the ooze and tangle.
　　And thus sailed my Hiawatha
Down the rushing Taquamenaw,
Sailed through all its bends and windings,
Sailed through all its deeps and shallows,
While his friend, the strong man, Kwasind,
Swam the deeps, the shallows waded.
　　Up and down the river went they,
In and out among its islands,
Cleared its bed of root and sand-bar,
Dragged the dead trees from its channel,
Made its passage safe and certain,
Made a pathway for the people,
From its springs among the mountains,
To the water of Pauwating,
To the bay of Taquamenaw.

THE PIED PIPER OF HAMELIN

Robert Browning

Browning wrote this poem, based on a thirteenth-century German legend, to amuse a small boy (William Macready, son of a famous actor) and sent it to him with the suggestion that he might draw illustrations for it.

Long afterwards, when the poet died, the drawings were found among his papers, along with a touching letter from the boy.

Hamelin Town's in Brunswick,
By famous Hanover city;
The river Weser, deep and wide,
Washes its wall on the southern side;
A pleasanter spot you never spied;
But, when begins my ditty,
Almost five hundred years ago,
To see the townsfolk suffer so
From vermin, was a pity.

Rats!
They fought the dogs, and killed the cats,
And bit the babies in the cradles,
And ate the cheeses out of the vats,
And licked the soup from the cooks' own ladles,
Split open the kegs of salted sprats,
Made nests inside men's Sunday hats,
And even spoiled the women's chats,
By drowning their speaking
With shrieking and squeaking
In fifty different sharps and flats.

At last the people in a body
To the Town Hall came flocking:
' 'Tis clear,' cried they, 'our Mayor's a noddy;
And as for our Corporation—shocking!
To think we buy gowns lined with ermine
For dolts than can't or won't determine
What's best to rid us of our vermin!
You hope, because you're old and obese,
To find in the furry civic robe ease?
Rouse up, Sirs! Give your brains a racking
To find the remedy we're lacking,
Or, sure as fate, we'll send you packing!'
At this the Mayor and Corporation
Quaked with a mighty consternation.

An hour they sat in council,
At length the Mayor broke silence:
'For a guilder I'd my ermine gown sell—
I wish I were a mile hence!
It's easy to bid one rack one's brain—
I'm sure my poor head aches again,
I've scratched it so, and all in vain.
Oh for a trap, a trap, a trap!'
Just as he said this, what should hap
At the chamber door, but a gentle tap?
'Bless us,' cried the Mayor, 'what's that?'
(With the Corporation as he sat,
Looking little though wondrous fat;
Nor brighter was his eye, nor moister
Than a too-long-opened oyster,
Save when at noon his paunch grew mutinous
For a plate of turtle green and glutinous.)
'Only a scraping of shoes on the mat!

Anything like the sound of a rat
Makes my heart go pit-a-pat!'

'Come in!'—the Mayor cried, looking bigger:
And in did come the strangest figure!
His queer long coat from heel to head
Was half of yellow and half of red;
And he himself was tall and thin,
With sharp blue eyes, each like a pin,
And light loose hair, yet swarthy skin,
No tuft on cheek nor beard on chin,
But lips where smiles went out and in—
There was no guessing his kith and kin!
And nobody could enough admire
The tall man and his quaint attire:
Quoth one: 'It's as my great-grandsire,
Starting up at the Trump of Doom's tone,
Had walked this way from his painted tombstone!'

He advanced to the council-table:
And, 'Please your honours,' said he, 'I'm able
By means of a secret charm to draw
All creatures living beneath the sun,
That creep or swim or fly or run,
After me so as you never saw!
And I chiefly use my charm
On creatures that do people harm,
The mole and toad and newt and viper;
And people call me the Pied Piper.'
(And here they noticed round his neck
A scarf of red and yellow stripe,
To match with his coat of the self-same check;
And at the scarf's end hung a pipe;
And his fingers, they noticed, were ever straying
As if impatient to be playing
Upon his pipe, as low it dangled
Over his vesture so old-fangled.)
'Yet,' said he, 'poor piper as I am,
In Tartary I freed the Cham,
Last June, from his huge swarms of gnats:
I eased in Asia the Nizam
Of a monstrous brood of vampyre-bats:
And as for what your brain bewilders,
If I can rid your town of rats
Will you give me a thousand guilders?'

'One? fifty thousand!'—was the exclamation
Of the astonished Mayor and Corporation.

Into the street the Piper stept,
Smiling first a little smile,
As if he knew what magic slept
In his quiet pipe the while;
Then, like a musical adept,
To blow the pipe his lips he wrinkled,
And green and blue his sharp eyes twinkled
Like a candle-flame where salt is sprinkled;
And ere three shrill notes the pipe uttered,
You heard as if an army muttered;
And the grumbling grew to a mighty rumbling;
And out of the houses the rats came tumbling.
Great rats, small rats, lean rats, brawny rats,
Brown rats, black rats, grey rats, tawny rats,
Grave old plodders, gay young friskers,
Fathers, mothers, uncles, cousins,
Cocking tails and pricking whiskers,
Families by tens and dozens,
Brothers, sisters, husbands, wives—
Followed the Piper for their lives.
From street to street he piped advancing,
And step for step they followed dancing,
Until they came to the river Weser
Wherein all plunged and perished!
—Save one who, stout as Julius Caesar,
Swam across and lived to carry
(As he the manuscript he cherished)
To Rat-land home his commentary:
Which was, 'At the first shrill notes of the pipe,
I heard a sound as of scraping tripe,
And putting apples, wondrous ripe,
Into a cider-press's gripe:
And a moving away of pickle-tub boards,
And a leaving ajar of conserve-cupboards,
And a drawing the corks of train-oil flasks,
And a breaking the hoops of butter-casks;
And it seemed as if a voice
(Sweeter far than by harp or by psaltery
Is breathed) called out, Oh rats, rejoice!
The world is grown to one vast dry-saltery!
So munch on, crunch on, take your nuncheon,
Breakfast, supper, dinner, luncheon!
And just as a bulky sugar-puncheon,

All ready staved, like a great sun shone
Glorious scarce an inch before me,
Just as methought it said, Come, bore me!
—I found the Weser rolling o'er me.'

You should have heard the Hamelin people
Ringing the bells till they rocked the steeple.
'Go,' cried the Mayor, 'and get long poles!
Poke out the nests and block up the holes!
Consult with carpenters and builders,
And leave in our town not even a trace
Of the rats!'—when suddenly, up the face
Of the Piper perked in the market-place,
With a 'First, if you please, my thousand guilders!'

A thousand guilders! The Mayor looked blue:
So did the Corporation too.
For council dinners made rare havoc
With Claret, Moselle, Vin-de-Grave, Hock;
And half the money would replenish
Their cellar's biggest butt with Rhenish.
To pay this sum to a wandering fellow
With a gipsy coat of red and yellow!
'Beside,' quoth the Mayor with a knowing wink,
'Our business was done at the river's brink;
We saw with our eyes the vermin sink,
And what's dead can't come to life, I think.
So, friend, we're not the folks to shrink
From the duty of giving you something to drink,
And a matter of money to put in your poke;
But as for the guilders, what we spoke
Of them, as you very well know, was in joke.
Besides, our losses have made us thrifty.
A thousand guilders! Come, take fifty!'

The Piper's face fell, and he cried,
'No trifling! I can't wait. Beside,
I've promised to visit by dinner time
Bagdad, and accept the prime
Of the Head-Cook's pottage, all he's rich in,
For having left, in the Caliph's kitchen,
Of a nest of scorpions no survivor—
With him I proved no bargain-driver,
With you, don't think I'll bate a stiver!
And folks who put me in a passion
May find me pipe to another fashion!'

'How?' cried the Mayor, 'd'ye think I'll brook
Being worse treated than a Cook?
Insulted by a lazy ribald
With idle pipe and vesture piebald?
You threaten us, fellow? Do your worst,
Blow your pipe there till you burst!'

Once more he stept into the street;
And to his lips again
Laid his long pipe of smooth straight cane;
And ere he blew three notes (such sweet
Soft notes as yet musician's cunning
Never gave the enraptured air)
There was a rustling, that seemed like a bustling
Of merry crowds justling at pitching and hustling,
Small feet were pattering, wooden shoes clattering,
Little hands clapping and little tongues chattering,
And, like fowls in a farm-yard when barley is scattering,
Out came the children running.
All the little boys and girls,
With rosy cheeks and flaxen curls,
And sparkling eyes and teeth like pearls,
Tripping and skipping, ran merrily after
The wonderful music with shouting and laughter.

The Mayor was dumb, and the Council stood
As if they were changed into blocks of wood,
Unable to move a step, or cry
To the children merrily skipping by—
And could only follow with the eye
That joyous crowd at the Piper's back.
But how the Mayor was on the rack,
And the wretched Council's bosoms beat,
As the Piper turned from the High Street
To where the Weser rolled its waters
Right in the way of their sons and daughters!
However he turned from South to West,
And to Koppelberg Hill his steps addressed,
And after him the children pressed;
Great was the joy in every breast
'He never can cross that mighty top!
He's forced to let the piping drop,
And we shall see our children stop!'
When, lo, as they reached the mountain's side,
A wondrous portal opened wide,

As if a cavern was suddenly hollowed;
And the Piper advanced and the children followed,
And when all were in to the very last,
The door in the mountain-side shut fast.

Did I say, all? No! One was lame,
And could not dance the whole of the way;
And in after years, if you would blame
His sadness, he was used to say,—
It's dull in our town since my playmates left!
I can't forget that I'm bereft
Of all the pleasant sights they see,
Which the Piper also promised me.
For he led us, he said, to a joyous land,
Joining the town and just at hand,
Where waters gushed and fruit-trees grew,
And flowers put forth a fairer hue,
And everything was strange and new;
The sparrows were brighter than peacocks here,
And their dogs outran our fallow deer,
And honey-bees had lost their stings,
And horses were born with eagles' wings:
And just as I became assured
My lame foot would be speedily cured,
The music stopped and I stood still,
And found myself outside the Hill,
Left alone against my will,
To go now limping as before,
And never hear of that country more!'

Alas, alas for Hamelin!
There came into many a burgher's pate
A text which says, that Heaven's Gate
Opes to the Rich at as easy rate
As the needle's eye takes a camel in!

The Mayor sent East, West, North and South,
To offer the Piper, by word of mouth,
Wherever it was men's lot to find him,
Silver and gold to his heart's content,
If he'd only return the way he went,
And bring the children behind him.
But when they saw 'twas a lost endeavour,
And Piper and dancers were gone for ever,
They made a decree that lawyers never
Should think their records dated duly

If, after the day of the month and year,
These words did not as well appear,
'And so long after what happened here
On the Twenty-second of July,
Thirteen-hundred and seventy-six;'
And the better in memory to fix
The place of the children's last retreat,
They called it, the Pied Piper's Street—
Where any one playing on pipe or tabor
Was sure for the future to lose his labour;
Nor suffered they hostelry or tavern
To shock with mirth a street so solemn;
But opposite the place of the cavern
They wrote the story on a column,
And on the great Church-Window painted
The same, to make the world acquainted
How their children were stolen away;
And there it stands to this very day.

And I must not omit to say
That in Transylvania there's a tribe
Of alien people that ascribe
The outlandish ways and dress
On which their neighbours lay such stress
To their fathers and mothers having risen
Out of some subterraneous prison
Into which they were trepanned
Long time ago in a mighty band
Out of Hamelin town in Brunswick land,
But how or why, they don't understand.

THE FORSAKEN MERMAN

Matthew Arnold

Come, dear children, let us away;
Down and away below!
Now my brothers call from the bay,
Now the great winds shoreward blow,
Now the salt tides seaward flow;

Now the wild white horses play,
Champ and chafe and toss in the spray.
Children dear, let us away!
This way, this way!

Call her once before you go—
Call once yet!
In a voice that she will know:
'Margaret! Margaret!'
Children's voices should be dear
(Call once more) to a mother's ear;
Children's voices, wild with pain—
Surely she will come again!

Call her once and come away;
This way, this way!
'Mother dear, we cannot stay!
The wild white horses foam and fret.'
Margaret! Margaret!

Come, dear children, come away down;
Call no more!
One last look at the white-wall'd town,
And the little grey church on the windy shore,
Then come down!
She will not come though you call all day;
Come away, come away!

Children dear, was it yesterday
We heard the sweet bells over the bay?
In the caverns where we lay,
Through the surf and through the swell,
The far-off sound of a silver bell?

Sand-strewn caverns, cool and deep,
Where the winds are all asleep;
Where the spent lights quiver and gleam,
Where the salt weed sways in the stream,
Where the sea-beasts, ranged all round,
Feed in the ooze of their pasture-ground;
Where the sea-snakes coil and twine,
Dry their mail and bask in the brine;
Where great whales come sailing by,
Sail and sail, with unshut eye,
Round the world for ever and aye?

When did music come this way?
Children dear, was it yesterday?

Children dear, was it yesterday
(Call yet once) that she went away?
Once she sate with you and me,
On a red gold throne in the heart of the sea,
And the youngest sate on her knee.
She comb'd its bright hair, and she tended it well,
When down swung the sound of a far-off bell.
She sigh'd, she look'd up through the clear green sea;
She said: 'I must go, for my kinsfolk pray
In the little grey church on the shore to-day.
'Twill be Easter-time in the world—ah me!
And I lose my poor soul, Merman! here with thee.'
I said: 'Go up, dear heart, through the waves;
Say thy prayer, and come back to the kind sea-caves!'
She smiled, she went up through the surf in the bay.
Children dear, was it yesterday?

Children dear, were we long alone?
'The sea grows stormy, the little ones moan;
Long prayers,' I said, 'in the world they say;
Come!' I said; and we rose through the surf in the bay.
We went up the beach, by the sandy down
Where the sea-stocks bloom, to the white-wall'd town;
Through the narrow paved streets, where all was still,
To the little grey church on the windy hill.
From the church came a murmur of folk at their prayers,
But we stood without in the cold blowing airs.
We climb'd on the graves, on the stones worn with rains,
And we gazed up the aisle through the small leaded panes.
She sate by the pillar; we saw her clear:
'Margaret, hist! come quick, we are here!
Dear heart,' I said, 'we are long alone;
The sea grows stormy, the little ones moan.'
But, ah, she gave me never a look,
For her eyes were seal'd to the holy book!
Loud prays the priest; shut stands the door.
Come away, children, call no more!
Come away, come down, call no more!

Down, down, down!
Down to the depths of the sea!
She sits at her wheel in the humming town,
Singing most joyfully.

Hark what she sings: 'O joy, O joy,
For the humming street, and the child with its toy;
For the priest, and the bell, and the holy well;
For the wheel where I spun,
And the blessed light of the sun!'
And so she sings her fill,
Singing most joyfully,
Till the spindle drops from her hand,
And the whizzing wheel stands still.
She steals to the window, and looks at the sand,
And over the sand at the sea;
And her eyes are set in a stare;
And anon there breaks a sigh,
And anon there drops a tear
From a sorrow-clouded eye,
And a heart sorrow-laden,
A long, long sigh
For the cold strange eyes of a little Mermaiden
And the gleam of her golden hair.

Come away, away children;
Come children, come down!
The hoarse wind blows coldly;
Lights shine in the town.
She will start from her slumber
When gusts shake the door;
She will hear the winds howling,
Will hear the waves roar.
We shall see, while above us
The waves roar and whirl,
A ceiling of amber,
A pavement of pearl.
Singing: 'Here came a mortal,
But faithless was she!
And alone dwell for ever
The kings of the sea.'

But, children, at midnight,
When soft the winds blow,
When clear falls the moonlight,
When spring-tides are low;
When sweet airs come seaward
From heaths starr'd with broom,
And high rocks throw mildly
On the blanch'd sands a gloom;
Up the still, glistening beaches,

Up the creeks we will hie,
Over banks of bright seaweed
The ebb-tide leaves dry.
We will gaze, from the sand-hills,
At the white, sleeping town;
At the church on the hill-side—
And then come back down.
Singing: 'There dwells a loved one,
But cruel is she!
She left lonely for ever
The kings of the sea.'

HORATIUS AT THE BRIDGE

Lord Macaulay

Horatius was a legendary Roman hero. After the city had been founded by Romulus and Remus it was ruled by kings. The Romans finally drove out their cruel kings and the idea of kingship was hated throughout the rest of Roman history.

The deposed Tarquins allied themselves with Lars Porsena, king of the neighbouring state of Etruria. The Etruscan army marched on Rome and was too powerful to be met in open battle. Rome lay behind the River Tiber, crossed by a single narrow wooden bridge; the defence of this bridge is the theme of Macaulay's poem.

Lars Porsena of Clusium
By the Nine Gods he swore
That the great house of Tarquin
Should suffer wrong no more.
By the Nine Gods he swore it,
And named a trysting-day,
And bade his messengers ride forth,
East and west and south and north,
To summon his array.

Fast by the royal standard,
O'erlooking all the war,
Lars Porsena of Clusium
Sat in his ivory car.
By the right wheel rode Mamilius,
Prince of the Latian name;
And by the left false Sextus,
That wrought the deed of shame.

But when the face of Sextus
Was seen among the foes,
A yell that rent the firmament
From all the town arose.
On the house-tops was no woman
But spat towards him and hissed,
No child but screamed out curses,
And shook its little fist.

But the Consul's brow was sad,
And the Consul's speech was low.
And darkly looked he at the wall
And darkly at the foe;
'Their van will be upon us
Before the bridge goes down;
And if they once may win the bridge,
What hope to save the town?'

Then out spake brave Horatius,
The Captain of the Gate :
'To every man upon this earth
Death cometh soon or late.
And how can man die better
Than facing fearful odds
For the ashes of his fathers
And the temples of his Gods?

'Hew down the bridge, Sir Consul,
With all the speed ye may;
I, with two more to help me,
Will hold the foe in play.
In yon strait path a thousand
May well be stopped by three :
Now who will stand on either hand
And keep the bridge with me?'

Then out spake Spurius Lartius,—
A Ramnian proud was he :
'Lo, I will stand at thy right hand,
And keep the bridge with thee.'
And out spake strong Herminius,—
Of Titian blood was he :
'I will abide on thy left side,
And keep the bridge with thee.'

'Horatius,' quoth the Consul,
'As thou sayest so let it be.'
And straight against that great array
Forth went the dauntless Three.
For Romans in Rome's quarrel
Spared neither land nor gold,
Nor son nor wife, nor limb nor life,
In the brave days of old.

Was none who would be foremost
To lead such dire attack;
But those behind cried 'Forward!'
And those before cried 'Back!'
And backwards now and forward
Wavers the deep array;
And on the tossing sea of steel
To and fro the standards reel,
And the victorious trumpet-peal
Dies fitfully away.

Yet one man for one moment
Stood out before the crowd:
Well known was he to all the Three,
And they gave him greeting loud:
'Now welcome, welcome, Sextus!
Now welcome to thy home!
Why dost thou stay, and turn away?
Here lies the road to Rome.'

Thrice looked he at the city;
Thrice looked he at the dead;
And thrice came on in fury,
And thrice turned back in dread;
And, white with fear and hatred,
Scowled at the narrow way
Where, wallowing in a pool of blood,
The bravest Tuscans lay.

But meanwhile axe and lever
Have manfully been plied;
And now the bridge hangs tottering
Above the boiling tide.
'Come back, come back, Horatius!'
Loud cried the Fathers all.—
'Back, Lartius! back, Herminius!
Back, ere the ruin fall!'

Back darted Spurius Lartius;—
Herminius darted back:
And, as they passed, beneath their feet
They felt the timbers crack.
But when they turned their faces,
And on the farther shore
Saw brave Horatius stand alone,
They would have crossed once more:

But with a crash like thunder
Fell every loosened beam,
And, like a dam, the mighty wreck
Lay right athwart the stream:
And a long shout of triumph
Rose from the walls of Rome,
As to the highest turret-tops
Was splashed the yellow foam.

And, like a horse unbroken,
When first he feels the rein,
The furious river struggled hard,
And tossed his tawny mane,
And burst the curb, and bounded,
Rejoicing to be free;
And whirling down, in fierce career,
Battlement, and plank, and pier,
Rushed headlong to the sea.

Alone stood brave Horatius,
But constant still in mind,—
Thrice thirty thousand foes before,
And the broad flood behind.
'Down with him!' cried false Sextus,
With a smile on his pale face;
'Now yield thee,' cried Lars Porsena,
'Now yield thee to our grace.'

Round turned he, as not deigning
Those craven ranks to see;
Naught spake he to Lars Porsena,
To Sextus naught spake he;
But he saw on Palatinus
The white porch of his home;
And he spake to the noble river
That rolls by the towers of Rome:

'Oh Tiber! Father Tiber!
To whom the Romans pray,
A Roman's life, a Roman's arms,
Take thou in charge this day!'
So he spake, and, speaking, sheathed
The good sword by his side,
And, with his harness on his back,
Plunged headlong in the tide,

No sound of joy or sorrow
Was heard from either bank,
But friends and foes in dumb surprise,
With parted lips and straining eyes,
Stood gazing where he sank;
And when above the surges
They saw his crest appear,
All Rome sent forth a rapturous cry,
And even the ranks of Tuscany
Could scarce forbear to cheer.

But fiercely ran the current,
Swollen high by months of rain;
And fast his blood was flowing,
And he was sore in pain,
And heavy with his armour,
And spent with changing blows;
And oft they thought him sinking,
But still again he rose.

Never, I ween, did swimmer,
In such an evil case,
Struggle through such a raging flood
Safe to the landing-place;
But his limbs were borne up bravely
By the brave heart within,
And our good Father Tiber
Bore bravely up his chin.

'Curse on him!' quoth false Sextus;—
'Will not the villain drown?
But for this stay, ere close of day
We should have sacked the town!'
'Heaven help him!' quoth Lars Porsena,
'And bring him safe to shore;
For such a gallant feat of arms
Was never seen before.'

And now he feels the bottom;
Now on dry earth he stands;
Now round him throng the Fathers
To press his gory hands;
And now, with shouts and clapping,
And noise of weeping loud,
He enters through the River-Gate,
Borne by the joyous crowd.

When the oldest cask is opened,
And the largest lamp is lit;
When the chestnuts glow in the embers,
And the kid turns on the spit;
When young and old in circle
Around the firebrands close;
When the girls are weaving baskets,
And the lads are shaping bows;

When the goodman mends his armour,
And trims his helmet's plume;
When the goodwife's shuttle merrily
Goes flashing through the loom;
With weeping and with laughter
Still is the story told,
How well Horatius kept the bridge
In the brave days of old.

SIR PATRICK SPENS

Anonymous

This ancient ballad is founded on fact but, as often happened, it was altered considerably in the course of being handed down from one story-teller to another.

The poem as we have it combines two incidents. In the reign of Alexander III of Scotland, his daughter Margaret was escorted by a large party of nobles to Norway for her marriage to King Eric; on the return journey many of them were drowned. Some twenty years later, when Alexander died, his grand-daughter Margaret, the Maid of Norway, was heiress to the Scottish throne, and on the voyage to Scotland she died.

The King sits in Dunfermline town,
Drinking the blood-red wine;
'O where shall I get a skeely skipper
To sail this ship of mine?'

Then up and spake an eldern knight,
Sat at the King's right knee:
'Sir Patrick Spens is the best sailor
That ever sailed the sea.'

The King has written a broad letter,
And sealed it with his hand,
And sent it to Sir Patrick Spens,
Was walking on the strand.

'To Noroway, to Noroway,
To Noroway o'er the foam;
The King's daughter of Noroway,
'Tis thou must fetch her home.'

The first line that Sir Patrick read,
A loud laugh laughéd he;
The next line that Sir Patrick read
The tear blinded his ee.

'O who is this has done this deed,
Has told the King of me,
To send us out at this time of the year,
To sail upon the sea?

'Be it wind, be it wet, be it hail, be it sleet,
Our ship must sail the foam;
The King's daughter of Noroway,
'Tis we must fetch her home.'

They hoisted their sails on Monenday morn,
With all the speed they may;
And they have landed in Noroway
Upon a Wodensday.

They had not been a week, a week,
In Noroway but twae,
When that the lords of Noroway
Began aloud to say,—

'Ye Scottishmen spend all our King's gowd,
And all our Queenis fee.'
'Ye lie, ye lie, ye liars loud!
So loud I hear ye lie.

'For I brought as much of the white monie
As gane my men and me,
And a half-fou of the good red gowd
Out o'er the sea with me.

'Make ready, make ready, my merry men all,
Our good ship sails the morn.'
'Now, ever alack, my master dear,
I fear a deadly storm.

'I saw the new moon late yestreen
With the old moon in her arm;
And if we go to sea, mastér,
I fear we'll come to harm.'

They had not sailed a league, a league,
A league but barely three,
When the lift grew dark, and the wind blew loud,
And gurly grew the sea.

The ankers brake and the top-masts lap,
It was such a deadly storm;
And the waves came o'er the broken ship
Till all her sides were torn.

'O where will I get a good sailór
Will take my helm in hand,
Till I get up to the tall top-mast
To see if I can spy land?'

'Oh here am I, a sailor good,
Will take the helm in hand,
Till you go up to the tall top-mast,
But I fear you'll ne'er spy land.'

He had not gone a step, a step,
A step but barely ane,
When a bolt flew out of the good ship's side,
And the salt sea it came in.

'Go fetch a web of the silken cloth,
Another of the twine,
And wap them into our good ship's side,
And let not the sea come in.'

They fetched a web of the silken cloth,
Another of the twine,
And they wapp'd them into the good ship's side,
But still the sea came in.

O loth, loth were our good Scots lords
To wet their cork-heel'd shoon,
But long ere all the play was play'd
They wet their hats aboon.

And many was the feather-bed
That fluttered on the foam;
And many was the good lord's son
That never more came home.

The ladies wrang their fingers white,
The maidens tore their hair,
All for the sake of their true loves,
For them they'll see nae mair.

O long, long may the ladies sit
With their fans into their hands,
Before they see Sir Patrick Spens
Come sailing to the strand.

And long, long may the maidens sit
With their gold combs in their hair,
All waiting for their own dear loves,
For them they'll see nae mair.

O forty miles off Aberdeen,
'Tis fifty fathoms deep;
And there lies good Sir Patrick Spens,
With the Scots lords at his feet.

THE LADY OF SHALOTT

Lord Tennyson

*The story of the Lady of Shalott comes from the legends about
King Arthur and the Knights of the Round Table. Among them were
Sir Lancelot, Sir Galahad and Sir Bedivere. Guinevere the queen,
Merlin the magician and the city of Camelot are other names linked
with Arthur and his land of Lyonesse.*

Part I

On either side the river lie
Long fields of barley and of rye,
That clothe the wold and meet the sky;
And thro' the field the road runs by
To many-tower'd Camelot;

And up and down the people go,
Gazing where the lilies blow
Round an island there below,
The island of Shalott.

Willows whiten, aspens quiver,
Little breezes dusk and shiver
Thro' the wave that runs for ever
By the island in the river
Flowing down to Camelot.
Four gray walls, and four gray towers,
Overlook a space of flowers,
And the silent isle imbowers
The Lady of Shalott.

By the margin, willow-veil'd,
Slide the heavy barges trail'd
By slow horses; and unhail'd
The shallop flitteth silken-sail'd
Skimming down to Camelot:
But who hath seen her wave her hand?
Or at the casement seen her stand?
Or is she known in all the land,
The Lady of Shalott?

Only reapers, reaping early
In among the bearded barley,
Hear a song that echoes cheerly
From the river winding clearly
Down to tower'd Camelot:
And by the moon the reaper weary,
Piling sheaves in uplands airy,
Listening, whispers ' 'Tis the fairy
Lady of Shalott.'

Part II

There she weaves by night and day
A magic web with colours gay.
She has heard a whisper say,
A curse is on her if she stay
To look down to Camelot.
She knows not what the curse may be,
And so she weaveth steadily,
And little other care hath she,
The Lady of Shalott.

And moving thro' a mirror clear
That hangs before her all the year,
Shadows of the world appear.
There she sees the highway near
Winding down to Camelot:
There the river eddy whirls,
And there the surly village-churls,
And the red cloaks of market girls,
Pass onward from Shalott.

Sometimes a troop of damsels glad,
An abbot on an ambling pad,
Sometimes a curly shepherd-lad,
Or long-hair'd page in crimson clad,
Goes by to tower'd Camelot;
And sometimes thro' the mirror blue
The knights come riding two and two:
She hath no loyal knight and true,
The Lady of Shalott.

But in her web she still delights
To weave the mirror's magic sights,
For often thro' the silent nights
A funeral, with plumes and lights
And music, went to Camelot:
Or when the moon was overhead,
Came two young lovers lately wed;
'I am half sick of shadows,' said
The Lady of Shalott.

Part III

A bow-shot from her bower-eaves,
He rode between the barley-sheaves,
The sun came dazzling thro' the leaves,
And flamed upon the brazen greaves
Of bold Sir Lancelot.
A red-cross knight for ever kneel'd
To a lady in his shield,
That sparkled on the yellow field,
Beside remote Shalott.

The gemmy bridle glitter'd free,
Like to some branch of stars we see
Hung in the golden Galaxy.
The bridle bells rang merrily
As he rode down to Camelot:

And from his blazon'd baldric slung
A mighty silver bugle hung,
And as he rode his armour rung,
Beside remote Shalott.

All in the blue unclouded weather
Thick-jewell'd shone the saddle-leather,
The helmet and the helmet-feather
Burn'd like one burning flame together,
As he rode down to Camelot.
As often thro' the purple night,
Below the starry clusters bright,
Some bearded meteor, trailing light,
Moves over still Shalott.

His broad clear brow in sunlight glow'd;
On burnish'd hooves his war-horse trode;
From underneath his helmet flow'd
His coal-black curls as on he rode,
As he rode down to Camelot.
From the bank and from the river
He flash'd into the crystal mirror,
'Tirra lirra,' by the river
Sang Sir Lancelot.

She left the web, she left the loom,
She made three paces thro' the room,
She saw the water-lily bloom,
She saw the helmet and the plume,
She look'd down to Camelot.
Out flew the web and floated wide;
The mirror crack'd from side to side;
'The curse is come upon me,' cried
The Lady of Shalott.

Part IV

In the stormy east-wind straining,
The pale yellow woods were waning,
The broad stream in his banks complaining,
Heavily the low sky raining
Over tower'd Camelot;
Down she came and found a boat
Beneath a willow left afloat,
And round about the prow she wrote
The Lady of Shalott.

And down the river's dim expanse
Like some bold seer in a trance,
Seeing all his own mischance—
With a glassy countenance
Did she look to Camelot.
And at the closing of the day
She loosed the chain, and down she lay;
The broad stream bore her far away
The Lady of Shalott.

Lying, robed in snowy white
That loosely flew to left and right—
The leaves upon her falling light—
Thro' the noises of the night
She floated down to Camelot:
And as the boat-head wound along
The willowy hills and fields among,
They heard her singing her last song,
The Lady of Shalott.

Heard a carol, mournful, holy,
Chanted loudly, chanted lowly,
Till her blood was frozen slowly,
And her eyes were darken'd wholly,
Turn'd to tower'd Camelot.
For ere she reach'd upon the tide
The first house by the water-side,
Singing in her song she died,
The Lady of Shalott.

Under tower and balcony,
By garden-wall and gallery,
A gleaming shape she floated by,
Dead-pale between the houses high,
Silent into Camelot.
Out upon the wharfs they came,
Knight and burgher, lord and dame,
And round the prow they read her name,
The Lady of Shalott.

Who is this? and what is here?
And in the lighted palace near
Died the sound of royal cheer;
And they cross'd themselves for fear.
All the knights at Camelot:

But Lancelot mused a little space;
He said, 'She has a lovely face;
God in his mercy lend her grace,
The Lady of Shalott.'

ROBIN HOOD AND ALAN-A-DALE

Anonymous

*This is another ballad, one of many about the outlaws who lived
in Sherwood Forest in mediaeval times. The adventure has a typical
motive, that of helping the weak against the strong, the poor against
the rich. It was this spirit that helped to make Robin Hood (Robber
i' the Wood?) popular with the country villagers.*

Come listen to me, you gallants so free,
All you that love mirth for to hear,
And I will you tell of a bold outlaw,
That lived in Nottinghamshire.

As Robin Hood in the forest stood,
All under the green-wood tree,
There was he ware of a brave young man,
As fine as fine might be.

The youngster was clothed in scarlet red,
In scarlet fine and gay,
And he did frisk it over the plain,
And chanted a roundelay.

As Robin Hood next morning stood,
Amongst the leaves so gay,
There did he espy the same young man
Come drooping along the way.

The scarlet he wore the day before,
It was clean cast away;
And every step he fetcht a sigh,
'Alack and well a day!'

Then steppèd forth brave Little John,
And Much the miller's son,
Which made the young man bend his bow,
When as he saw them come.

'Stand off, stand off!' the young man said,
'What is your will with me?'—
'You must come before our master straight,
Under yon green-wood tree.'

And when he came bold Robin before,
Robin askt him courteously,
'O hast thou any money to spare,
For my merry men and me?'

'I have no money,' the young man said,
'But five shillings and a ring;
And that I have kept this seven long years,
To have it at my wedding.

'Yesterday I should have married a maid,
But she is now from me tane,
And chosen to be an old knight's delight,
Whereby my poor heart is slain.'

'What is thy name?' then said Robin Hood,
'Come, tell me, without any fail.'—
'By the faith of my body,' then said the young man,
'My name is Alan-a-Dale.'

'What wilt thou give me,' said Robin Hood,
'In ready gold or fee,
To help thee to thy true-love again,
And deliver her unto thee?'

'I have no money,' then quoth the young man,
'No ready gold nor fee,
But I will swear upon a book
Thy true servant for to be.'—

'But how many miles to thy true-love?
Come tell me without any guile.'—
'By the faith of my body,' then said the young man,
'It is but five little mile,'

Then Robin he hasted over the plain,
He did neither stint nor lin,[1]
Until he came unto the church
Where Alan should keep his wedding.

---

[1] lin = stop.

'What dost thou do here?' the Bishop he said,
'I prithee now tell to me:'
'I am a bold harper,' quoth Robin Hood,
'And the best in the north countrey.'

'O welcome, O welcome!' the Bishop he said,
'That musick best pleaseth me.'—
'You shall have no musick,' quoth Robin Hood,
'Till the bride and the bridegroom I see.'

With that came in a wealthy knight,
Which was both grave and old,
And after him a finikin lass,
Did shine like glistering gold.

'This is no fit match,' quoth bold Robin Hood,
'That you do seem to make here;
For since we are come unto the church,
The bride she shall chuse her own dear.'

Then Robin Hood put his horn to his mouth,
And blew blasts two or three;
When four and twenty bowmen bold
Came leaping over the lee.

And when they came into the churchyard,
Marching all on a row,
The first man was Alan-a-Dale,
To give bold Robin his bow.

'This is thy true-love,' Robin he said,
'Young Alan, as I hear say;
And you shall be married at this same time,
Before we depart away.'

'That shall not be,' the Bishop he said,
'For thy word it shall not stand;
They shall be three times askt in the church,
As the law is of our land.'

Robin Hood pull'd off the Bishop's coat,
And put it upon Little John;
'By the faith of my body,' then Robin said,
'This cloath doth make thee a man.'

When Little John went into the quire,
The people began for to laugh;
He askt them seven times in the church,
Lest three should not be enough.

'Who gives me this maid?' then said Little John;
Quoth Robin. 'That do I!
And he that doth take her from Alan-a-Dale
Full dearly he shall her buy.'

And thus having ended this merry wedding,
The bride lookt as fresh as a queen,
And so they return'd to the merry green-wood,
Amongst the leaves so green.

THE HIGH TIDE ON THE COAST OF
LINCOLNSHIRE, 1571

Jean Ingelow

*This poem was written in the nineteenth century about an ancient
tragedy, a sudden flood caused by some unusual combination of
wind and tide and a river running high. 'Eygre' is an old word for
a kind of tidal wave that was the result.*

The old mayor climbed the belfry tower,
The ringers ran by two, by three;
'Pull, if ye never pulled before;
Good ringers, pull your best,' quoth he.
'Play uppe, play uppe, O Boston bells!
Ply all your changes, all your swells,
Play uppe, "The Brides of Enderby"!'

Men say it was a stolen tyde,—
The Lord that sent it, he knows all;
But in myne ears doth still abide
The message that the bells let fall:
And there was naught of strange, beside
The flight of mews and peewits pied,
By millions crouched on the old sea-wall.

I sat and spun within the doore,
My thread brake off, I raised myne eyes!
The level sun, like ruddy ore,
Lay sinking in the barren skies;
And dark against day's golden death
She moved where Lindis wandereth,—
My sonne's faire wife, Elizabeth.

'Cusha! Cusha! Cusha!' calling,
Ere the early dews were falling,
Farre away I heard her song.
'Cusha! Cusha!' all along,
Where the reedy Lindis floweth,
Floweth, floweth,
From the meads where melick groweth
Faintly came her milking song.

'Cusha! Cusha! Cusha!' calling,
'For the dews will soone be falling;
Leave your meadow grasses mellow,
Mellow, mellow;
Quit your cowslips, cowslips yellow;
Come uppe, Whitefoot, come uppe, Lightfoot,
Quit the stalks of parsley hollow,
Hollow, hollow;
Come uppe, Jetty, rise and follow,
From the clovers lift your head;
Come uppe, Whitefoot, come uppe, Lightfoot,
Come uppe, Jetty, rise and follow,
Jetty, to the milking-shed.'

If it be long, aye, long ago,
When I beginne to think howe long,
Againe I hear the Lindis flow,
Swift as an arrow, sharpe and strong;
And all the aire it seemeth mee
Bin full of floating bells (sayeth shee),
That ring the tune of Enderby.

Alle fresh the level pasture lay,
And not a shadowe mote be seene,
Save where, full fyve good miles away,
The steeple towered from out the greene;
And lo! the great bell farre and wide
Was heard in all the countryside
That Saturday at eventide.

The swannerds where their sedges are
Moved on in sunset's golden breath,
The shepherd lads I heard afarre,
And my sonne's wife, Elizabeth;
Till floating o'er the grassy sea
Came downe that kyndly message free,
The 'Brides of Mavis Enderby'.

Then some looked uppe into the sky,
And all along where Lindis flows
To where the goodly vessels lie,
And where the lordly steeple shows.
They sayde, 'And why should this thing be?
What danger lowers by land or sea?
They ring the tune of Enderby!

'For evil news from Mablethorpe,
Of pyrate galleys warping downe;
For shippes ashore beyond the scorpe,
They have not spared to wake the towne;
But while the west bin red to see,
And storms be none, and pyrates flee,
Why ring "The Brides of Enderby"?'

I looked without, and lo! my sonne
Came riding downe with might and main.
He raised a shout as he drew on,
Till all the welkin rang again,
'Elizabeth! Elizabeth'
(A sweeter woman ne'er drew breath
Than my sonne's wife, Elizabeth.)

'The olde sea wall (he cried) is downe,
The rising tide comes on apace,
And boats adrift in yonder towne
Go sailing uppe the market-place.'
He shook as one that looks on death:
'God save you, mother!' straight he sayeth;
'Where is my wife, Elizabeth?'

'Good sonne, where Lindis winds away
With her two bairns I marked her long;
And ere yon bells beganne to play,
Afar I heard her milking song.'

He looked across the grassy sea,
To right, to left, 'Ho, Enderby!'
They rang 'The Brides of Enderby'!

With that he cried and beat his breast;
For lo! along the river's bed
A mighty eygre reared his crest,
And uppe the Lindis raging sped.
It swept with thunderous noises loud;
Shaped like a curling snow-white cloud,
Or like a demon in a shroud.

And rearing Lindis backward pressed,
Shook all her trembling bankes amaine;
Then madly at the eygre's breast
Flung uppe her weltering walls again.
Then bankes came down with ruin and rout,—
Then beaten foam flew round about,—
Then all the mighty floods were out.

So farre, so fast the eygre drave,
The heart had hardly time to beat,
Before a shallow, seething wave
Sobbed in the grasses at our feet:
The feet had hardly time to flee
Before it brake against the knee,
And all the world was in the sea.

Upon the roofe we sate that night,
The noise of bells went sweeping by:
I marked the lofty beacon light
Stream from the church-tower, red and high,—
A lurid mark and dread to see;
And awesome bells they were to me,
That in the dark rang 'Enderby'.

They rang the sailor lads to guide
From roofe to roofe who fearless rowed
And I—my sonne was at my side,
And yet the ruddy beacon glowed:
And yet he moaned beneath his breath,
O come in life, or come in death!
O lost! my love, Elizabeth.'

And didst thou visit him no more?
Thou didst, thou didst, my daughter deare!
The waters laid thee at his doore,
Ere yet the early dawn was clear.
Thy pretty bairns in fast embrace,
The lifted sun shone on thy face,
Downe drifted to thy dwelling-place.

That flow strewed wrecks about the grass;
That ebbe swept out the flocks to sea;
A fatal ebbe and flow, alas!
To manye more than myne and mee:
But each will mourn his own (she sayeth).
And sweeter woman ne'er drew breath
Than my sonne's wife, Elizabeth.

I shall never hear her more
By the reedy Lindis' shore,
'Cusha, Cusha, Cusha!' calling,
Ere the early dews be falling;
I shall never hear her song,
'Cusha! Cusha,' all along,
Where the sunny Lindis floweth,
Floweth, floweth;
From the meads where melick groweth,
When the water winding down,
Onward floweth to the town.

I shall never see her more
Where the reeds and rushes quiver,
Shiver, quiver:
Stand beside the sobbing river,
Sobbing, throbbing, in its falling,
To the sandy lonesome shore,
I shall never hear her calling,
'Leave your meadow grasses mellow,
Mellow, mellow;
Quit your cowslips, cowslips yellow;
Come uppe, Whitefoot, come uppe, Lightfoot;
Quit your pipes of parsley hollow,
Hollow, hollow:
Come uppe, Lightfoot, rise and follow;
Lightfoot, Whitefoot,
From your clovers lift the head;
Come uppe, Jetty, follow, follow,
Jetty, to the milking-shed.'

THE HIGHWAYMAN

Alfred Noyes

Highwaymen were comparatively common in England in the eighteenth century. At that time the roads were sufficiently improved for travel by coach to be practicable, but there was no police force and it was difficult to enforce the king's justice outside the towns. Highwaymen were simply robbers, of course, but their exploits aroused some degree of sympathy, especially among the poor.

Part One

The wind was a torrent of darkness among the gusty trees,
The moon was a ghostly galleon tossed upon cloudy seas,
The road was a ribbon of moonlight over the purple moor,
And the highwayman came riding—
Riding—riding—
The highwayman came riding, up to the old inn-door.

He'd a French cocked-hat on his forehead, a bunch of lace at
 his chin,
A coat of the claret velvet, and breeches of brown doeskin;
They fitted with never a wrinkle: his boots were up to the
 thigh!
And he rode with a jewelled twinkle,
His pistol butts a-twinkle,
His rapier hilt a-twinkle, under the jewelled sky.

Over the cobbles he clattered and clashed in the dark inn-
 yard,
And he tapped with his whip on the shutters, but all was
 locked and barred;
He whistled a tune to the window, and who should be waiting
 there
But the landlord's black-eyed daughter,
Bess, the landlord's daughter,
Plaiting a dark red love-knot into her long black hair.

And dark in the dark old inn-yard a stable-wicket creaked
Where Tim the ostler listened; his face was white and peaked;
His eyes were hollows of madness, his hair like mouldy hay,

But he loved the landlord's daughter.
The landlord's red-lipped daughter,
Dumb as a dog he listened, and he heard the robber say—

'One kiss, my bonny sweetheart, I'm after a prize to-night,
But I shall be back with the yellow gold before the morning
        light;
Yet, if they press me sharply, and harry me through the day,
Then look for me by moonlight,
Watch for me by moonlight,
I'll come to thee by moonlight, though hell should bar the
        way.'

He rose upright in the stirrups, he scarce could reach her
        hand,
But she loosened her hair i' the casement! His face burnt like
        a brand
As the black cascade of perfume came tumbling over his
        breast;
And he kissed its waves in the moonlight,
(Oh sweet, black waves in the moonlight!)
Then he tugged at his rein in the moonlight, and galloped
        away to the west.

Part Two

He did not come in the dawning; he did not come at noon;
And out o' the tawny sunset, before the rise o' the moon,
When the road was a gypsy's ribbon, looping the purple moor,
A red-coat troop came marching—
Marching—marching—
King George's men came marching, up to the old inn-door.

They said no word to the landlord, they drank his ale instead.
But they gagged his daughter, and bound her to the foot of her
        narrow bed.
Two of them knelt at her casement, with muskets at their
        side!
There was death at every window;
And hell at one dark window;
For Bess could see, through her casement, the road that *he*
        would ride.

They had tied her up to attention, with many a sniggering
    jest;
They had bound a musket beside her, with the muzzle beneath
    her breast!
'Now, keep good watch!' and they kissed her.
    She heard the dead man say—
Look for me by moonlight;
Watch for me by moonlight;
I'll come to thee by moonlight, though hell should bar the
    way!

She twisted her hands behind her; but all the knots held good!
She writhed her hands till her fingers were wet with sweat
    or blood!
They stretched and strained in the darkness, and the hours
    crawled by like years,
Till, now, on the stroke of midnight,
    Cold, on the stroke of midnight,
The tip of one finger touched it! The trigger at least was hers!

The tip of one finger touched it; she strove no more for the
    rest!
Up, she stood up to attention, with the muzzle beneath her
    breast.
She would not risk their hearing; she would not strive again;
For the road lay bare in the moonlight;
    Blank and bare in the moonlight;
And the blood of her veins, in the moonlight, throbbed to her
    love's refrain.

Tlot-tlot; tlot-tlot! Had they heard it? The horse-hoofs ringing
    clear;
Tlot-tlot, tlot-tlot, in the distance? Were they deaf that they
    did not hear?
Down the ribbon of moonlight, over the brow of the hill,
The highwayman came riding,
    Riding, riding!
The red-coats looked to their priming! She stood up straight
    and still.

Tlot-tlot, in the frosty silence! *Tlot-tlot,* in the echoing night!
Nearer he came and nearer! Her face was like a light!
Her eyes grew wide for a moment; she drew one last deep
    breath,

Then her finger moved in the moonlight,
Her musket shattered the moonlight,
Shattered her breast in the moonlight and warned him—with
    her death.

He turned; he spurred to the westward; he did not know who
    stood
Bowed, with her head o'er the musket, drenched with her own
    blood!
Not till the dawn he heard it, and his face grew grey to hear
How Bess, the landlord's daughter,
The landlord's black-eyed daughter,
Had watched for her love in the moonlight, and died in the
    darkness there.

Back he spurred like a madman, shouting a curse to the sky,
With the white road smoking behind him and his rapier
    brandished high!
Blood-red were his spurs i' the golden noon; wine-red was his
    velvet coat;
When they shot him down on the highway,
Down like a dog on the highway,
And he lay in his blood on the highway, with a bunch of lace
    at his throat.

And still of a winter's night, they say, when the wind is in the
    trees,
When the moon is a ghostly galleon tossed upon cloudy seas,
When the road is a ribbon of moonlight over the purple moor,
A highwayman comes riding—
Riding—riding—
A highwayman comes riding, up to the old inn-door.

Over the cobbles he clatters and clangs in the dark inn-yard,
He taps with his whip on the shutters, but all is locked and
    barred;
He whistles a tune to the window, and who should be waiting
    there
But the landlord's black-eyed daughter,
Bess, the landlord's daughter,
Plaiting a dark red love-knot into her long black hair.

PAUL REVERE'S RIDE

Henry Wadsworth Longfellow

Paul Revere was an American patriot at the time of the struggle for independence. He was one of the leaders in the Boston 'tea-party'. He is remembered for his famous ride from Charlestown to Lexington on 18–19 April, 1775, to give warning of the approach of British troops. The engagement that followed was the beginning of the War of American Independence.

Listen, my children, and you shall hear
Of the midnight ride of Paul Revere
On the eighteenth of April, in Seventy-five;
Hardly a man is now alive
Who remembers that famous day and year.

He said to his friend, 'If the British march
By land or sea from the town to-night,
Hang a lantern aloft in the belfry arch
Of the North Church tower as a signal light,—
One, if by land, or two, if by sea;
And I on the opposite shore will be,
Ready to ride and spread the alarm
Through every Middlesex village and farm,
For the country-folk to be up and to arm,'
Then he said, 'Good night!' and with muffled oar
Silently rowed to the Charlestown shore,
Just as the moon rose over the bay,
Where swinging wide at her moorings lay
The Somerset, British man-of-war;
A phantom ship, with each mast and spar
Across the moon like a prison bar,
And a huge black hulk, that was magnified
By its own reflection in the tide.

Meanwhile, his friend, through alley and street,
Wanders and watches with eager ears,
Till in silence around him he hears
The muster of men at the barrack door,
The sound of drums, and the tramp of feet,
And the measured tread of the grenadiers,
Marching down to their boats on the shore.

Then he climbed to the tower of the church,
Up the wooden stairs, with stealthy tread,
To the belfry-chamber overhead,
And startled the pigeons from their perch
On the sombre rafters, that round him made
Masses and moving shapes of shade—
Up the trembling ladder, steep and tall,
To the highest window in the wall,
Where he paused to listen and look down
A moment on the roofs of the town,
And the moonlight flowing over all.

Beneath, in the churchyard, lay the dead,
In their night-encampment on the hill,
Wrapped in silence so deep and still
That he could hear, like a sentinel's tread,
The watchful night-wind, as it went
Creeping along from tent to tent,
And seeming to whisper, 'All is well!'
A moment only he feels the spell
Of the place and the hour, and the secret dread
Of the lonely belfry and the dead;
For suddenly all his thoughts are bent
On a shadowy something far away,
Where the river widens to meet the bay,—
A line of black that bends and floats
On the rising tide, like a bridge of boats.

Meanwhile, impatient to mount and ride,
Booted and spurred, with a heavy stride
On the opposite shore walked Paul Revere.
Now he patted his horse's side,
Now gazed at the landscape far and near,
Then, impetuous, stamped the earth,
And turned and tightened his saddle-girth;
But mostly he watched with eager search
The belfry-tower of the Old North Church,
As it rose above the graves on the hill,
Lonely and spectral and sombre and still,
And lo! as he looks, on the belfry's height
A glimmer, and then a gleam of light!
He springs to the saddle, the bridle he turns,
But lingers and gazes, till full on his sight
A second lamp in the belfry burns!

A hurry of hoofs in a village street,
A shape in the moonlight, a bulk in the dark,
And beneath, from the pebbles in passing, a spark
Struck out by a steed flying fearless and fleet;
That was all! And yet, through the gloom and the light,
The fate of a nation was riding that night;
And the spark struck out by that steed, in his flight,
Kindled the land into flame with its heat.

He has left the village and mounted the steep,
And beneath him, tranquil and broad and deep,
Is the Mystic, meeting the ocean tides;
And under the alders that skirt its edge,
Now soft on the sand, now loud on the ledge,
Is heard the tramp of his steed as he rides.

It was twelve by the village clock
When he crossed the bridge into Medford town.
He heard the crowing of the cock,
And the barking of the farmer's dog,
And felt the damp of the river fog,
That rises after the sun goes down.

It was one by the village clock,
When he galloped into Lexington.
He saw the gilded weathercock
Swim in the moonlight as he passed,
And the meeting-house windows, blank and bare,
Gaze at him with a spectral glare,
As if they already stood aghast
At the bloody work they would look upon.

It was two by the village clock,
When he came to the bridge in Concord town.
He heard the bleating of the flock,
And the twitter of birds among the trees,
And felt the breath of the morning breeze
Blowing over the meadows brown.
And one was safe and asleep in his bed
Who at the bridge would be first to fall,
Who that day would be lying dead,
Pierced by a British musket-ball.

You know the rest. In the books you have read,
How the British Regulars fired and fled,—
How the farmers gave them ball for ball,
From behind each fence and farmyard wall,

Chasing the red-coats down the lane,
Then crossing the fields to emerge again
Under the trees at the turn of the road,
And only pausing to fire and load.

So through the night rode Paul Revere;
And so through the night went his cry of alarm
To every Middlesex village and farm,—
A cry of defiance and not of fear,
A voice in the darkness, a knock at the door,
And a word that shall echo for evermore!

For, borne on the night-wind of the Past,
Through all our history, to the last,
In the hour of darkness and peril and need
The people will waken and listen to hear
The hurrying hoof-beats of that steed,
And the midnight message of Paul Revere.

JESSE JAMES

William Rose Benét

*Jesse James was an American outlaw who lived in the Mid-West in
the period just after the Civil War—less than a hundred years ago.
He was famous for robbing banks and railways and he was popu-
larly regarded as a hero.*

Jesse James was a two-gun man,
(Roll on, Missouri!)
Strong-arm chief of an outlaw clan.
(From Kansas to Illinois!)
He twirled an old Colt forty-five;
(Roll on, Missouri!)
They never took Jesse James alive.
(Roll, Missouri, roll!)

Jesse James was King of the Wes';
(Cataracks in the Missouri!)
He'd a di'mon' heart in his lef' breas';
(Brown Missouri rolls!)

He'd a fire in his heart no hurt could stifle;
(Thunder, Missouri!)
Lion eye an' a Winchester rifle.
(Missouri, roll down!)

Jesse James rode a pinto hawse;
Come at night to a water-cawse;
Tetched with the rowel that pinto's flank;
She sprung the torrent from bank to bank.

Jesse rode through a sleepin' town;
Looked the moonlit street both up an' down;
Crack-crack-crack, the street ran flames
An' a great voice cried, 'I'm Jesse James!'

Hawse an' afoot they're after Jess!
(Roll on, Missouri!)
Spurrin' an' spurrin'—but he's gone Wes'.
(Brown Missouri rolls!)
He was ten foot tall when he stood in his boots;
(Lightnin' light the Missouri!)
More'n a match fer sich galoots.
(Roll, Missouri, roll!)

Jesse James rode outa the sage;
Roun' the rocks come the swayin' stage;
Straddlin' the road a giant stan's
An' a great voice bellers, 'Throw up yer han's!'

Jesse raked in the di'mon' rings,
The big gold watches an' the yuther things;
Jesse divvied 'em then an' thar
With a cryin' child had lost her mar.

The U.S. troopers is after Jess;
(Roll on, Missouri!)
Their hawses sweat foam, but he's gone Wes';
(Hear Missouri roar!)
He was broad as a b'ar, he'd a ches' like a drum,
(Wind an' rain through Missouri!)
An' his red hair flamed like Kingdom Come.
(Missouri down to the sea!)

Jesse James all alone in the rain
Stopped an' stuck up the Eas'-boun' train;
Swayed through the coaches with horns an' a tail,
Lit out with the bullion an' the registered mail.

Jess made 'em all turn green with fright,
Quakin' in the aisles in the pitch-black night;
An' he give all the bullion to a pore ole tramp
Campin' nigh the cuttin' in the dirt an' damp.

The whole U.S. is after Jess;
(Roll on, Missouri!)
The son-of-a-gun, if he ain't gone Wes';
(Missouri to the sea!)
He could chaw cold iron an' spit blue flame;
(Cataracks down the Missouri!)
He rode on a catamount he'd larned to tame.
(Hear that Missouri roll!)

Jesse James rode into a bank;
Give his pinto a tetch on the flank;
Jumped the teller's window with an awful crash;
Heaved up the safe an' twirled his mustache;
He said, 'So long, boys!' He yelped, 'So long!
Feelin' porely today—I ain't feelin' strong!'
Rode right through the wall a-goin' crack-crack-crack—
Took the safe home to mother in a gunny-sack.

They're creepin', they're crawlin', they're stalkin' Jess;
(Roll on, Missouri!)
They's word of a cayuse hitched to the bars
(Ruddy clouds on Missouri!)
Of a golden sunset that busts into stars.
(Missouri, roll down!)

Jesse James rode hell fer leather;
He was a hawse an' a man together;
In a cave in a mountain high up in air
He lived with a rattlesnake, a wolf, an' a bear.

Jesse's heart was as sof' as a woman;
Fer guts an' stren'th he was sooper-human;
He could put six shots through a woodpecker's eye
And take in one swaller a gallon o' rye.

They sought him here an' they sought him there,
(Roll on, Missouri!)
But he strides by night through the ways of the air;
(Brown Missouri rolls!)
They say he was took an' they say he is dead,
(Thunder Missouri!)
But he ain't—he's a sunset overhead!
(Missouri down to the sea!)

Jesse James was a Hercules.
When he went through the woods he tore up the trees.
When he went on the plains he smoked the groun'
An' the hull lan' shuddered fer miles aroun'.

Jesse James wore a red bandanner
That waved on the breeze like the Star Spangled Banner;
In seven states he cut up dadoes.
He's gone with the buffler an' the desperadoes.

Yes, Jesse James was a two-gun man
(Roll on, Missouri!)
The same as when this song began;
(From Kansas to Illinois!)
An' when you see a sunset burst into flames
(Lightnin' light the Missouri!)
Or a thunderstorm blaze—thar's Jesse James!
(Hear that Missouri roll!)

THE 'JERVIS BAY'

Michael Thwaites

The 'Jervis Bay' was originally a liner sailing between England and Australia. On the outbreak of war she was converted to an armed merchant cruiser carrying six-inch guns. In November, 1940 she was escorting an Atlantic convoy of thirty-seven ships when they were attacked by a German battleship; an unequal action followed, but it gained enough time for all except five of the convoy to escape. The introductory part of the poem is not given here.

But the days and the weeks and the months ran on, with little
        to see or show
But the endless empty Atlantic, with the convoys to and fro,
And it was the fifth of November, and the sun getting low.

In the dusk of the evening the wolf is abroad,
He crouches in the valley at the lonely ford
Where the sheep come down. What help have the sheep?
They must all be slaughtered when the wolf shall leap.

The sheep have the sheepdog. But what can he do,
With his slow old legs and his teeth so few?
He could meet the jackal and never fear,
Or the slinking fox; but the wolf is here
—That steely strength, that merciless art.
He has few old teeth, but a lion's heart.

On either side the *Jervis Bay* the convoy was dipping,
And the Captain as he paced the bridge paused, one hand
    gripping
A stanchion, to study them against the amber rim
Of sky—the ships whose safety was entrusted to him.
They spread, a broad battalion, massed in column nine abreast,
There *Trewellard*, *Cornish City*, *San Demetrio*—North-by-
    West
Was it smoke or cloud?—*Castillian*, *Rangitiki*, and the rest.
Satisfied, he turned to go below; when a sudden gleam
Flickered in the north, and a shout from the lookout, 'Ship
    on the port beam.'
Two seconds, and Captain Fegen's glasses rake the horizon to
    norrard,
Two more, and the bells ring Action Stations. Aft, amid-ships,
    forrard,
The guns are manned loaded and trained—the crews were
    standing by—
And the men below are running to their stations, and every
    pulse beats high.
And Fegen's pulse is racing hard, but his eye is steady and
    clear,
And the smudge on the horizon shimmers into shape, and is
    the *Admiral Scheer*.
The telegraph clangs to 'Full Ahead'. Her great heart pound-
    ing,
The *Jervis Bay* trembles and surges forward, sounding
The alarm on her siren. From her bridge the Aldis chatters
To an answering flicker from where the Commodore scatters
The foaming seas, awaiting his orders for the convoy.
'Warship, thought hostile, my port beam.' An envoy
Of wrath, a white column spouts sudden and high
Topping the mast. A detonation shakes the sea and sky.
'Scatter under smoke.'—Fluttering flags and sirens blowing
Down the columns of the convoy.—But the *Jervis Bay* is
    going
Steady onward as they turn. From the smoke floats are flowing
Streams of velvet solid smoke drifting over the ocean swell.
But the enemy gunners knew their job. A salvo of shell

Roars in the sea—one, two, three—by the *Rangitiki*'s bow
As she twists in flight. Already they have found for line,
And now
A salvo spouts alongside—the iron jaws closing
On the vulnerable spine. Now the convoy are nosing
East, south, west, away fanwise are scattering,
But the shells fall like drops in thunder ominously pattering.
And Captain Fegen had that day a second, or maybe two,
As he stood on the bridge of the *Jervis Bay*, to choose what he
    would do.
Astern of him the convoy, labouring heavily in flight,
And one long hour till they could win to cover of the night.
To port the Nazi battleship, with nine eleven-inch guns
Three over three in turrets ranged to hurl their angry tons
Of blasting steel across the miles his guns could never span,
With twice his speed, with a Naval crew, trained expert to a
    man,
With armour-plated sides and deck, a warship through and
    through,
The pride of the German builders' craft. All this Fegen knew.
Knew his foeman as he came in overmastering might,
Knew well there was no hope at all in such unequal fight,
Knew his own unarmoured sides, his few old six-inch guns,
His fourteen meagre knots, his men, their country's sturdy
    sons,
But hasty-trained and still untried in the shock and din of
    action.
To starboard were the merchantmen, and he was their protec-
    tion.

Rarely it comes, and unforeseen,
In the life of a man, a community, a nation,
The moment that knits up struggling diversity
In one, the changing transverse lights
Focussed to a pin-point's burning intensity,
Rarely and unforeseen.
But in the minute is the timeless and absolute
Fulfilment of centuries and civilisations,
When the temporal skin lays bare the eternal bone,
And this mortal puts on immortality.
In that stark flash the unregarding universe
Is a hushed agony. The suns and planets
Stay : the dewdrop dares not tremble :
The dead leaf in the electric air
Waits : and the waterfall still as a photograph
Hangs in that intolerable minute.

And the dead and the living, all are there
With those that shall be, all Creation
Pausing poised in the ticking of Eternity,
Held at one white point of crisis.
But what does he know, he at the focus,
The man or the nation? Joy and terror he knows,
But chiefly a blessed sweet release,
The complex equation at a stroke resolved
To simple terms, a single choice,
Rarely and unforeseen.
So Fegen stood, and Time dissolved,
And Cradock with his ships steamed out
From Coronel, and in the pass
Of Roncesvalles a horn was sounding,
And Oates went stumbling out alone
Into that Antarctic night,
And Socrates the hemlock drank
And paid his debts and laid him down,
And through the fifty-three, *Revenge*
Ran on, as in Thermopylæ
The cool-eyed Spartans looked about,
Childe Roland, trembling, took and blew,
The *Jervis Bay* went hard-a-port.
'Hard-a-port' and 'Hard-a-port, sir.' The white spray flying,
She heeled and turned and steadied her course for where the
        foe was lying,
And not a man but knew the fate that he had turned to meet
And yet was stirred to fight till death and never know retreat.
'Salvoes, fire.' Her guns speak, but they are old and worn,
The shots fall in the water, short. The raider as in scorn
Keeps his fire on the convoy still, now veiled in smoke, now
        clear,
But the *Jervis Bay* is closing fast and her shots are creeping
        near.
And now he swings on her his turrets, as a thief surprised
        might turn.
His anger thunders near, ahead. She trembles from stem to
        stern.
A flash, and she staggers, as through her egg-shell plates
Tear the eleven-inch projectiles, malevolent as the Fates.
And smoke pouring and wreckage flying as the shells fall like
        rain,
But she fights, and the convoy are scattering fast, and every
        minute is gain.
'Am closing the enemy,' Fegen signals. She heaves, and is hit
        again.

Now the wolf is among the flock,
The sheep are leaping to ledge and rock
Like scattered clouds. To left and right
The wolf is at work and his teeth are white,
His teeth are white and quick is he.
Soon the flock will cease to be
That grazed along so peaceably.
But suddenly the sheepdog comes
With growling as a roll of drums,
Stiff and heavy, eyes a-blear,
But he knows the wolf is near,
And within the agèd brain
One thought only may remain,
Headlong as he hurls himself
At the grey throat of the wolf
Where his old teeth sink and stay.

But he, with fury and dismay,
Drops his kill and turns to tear
The creature that affronts him there.
This way and that he rends and claws
But cannot break those ancient jaws
That never while they live relax,
While flanks are torn and sinew cracks
And haunch a mangled tatter lies
And the blood runs in his eyes,
And, hanging so, he dies.

And it is cold and it is night
Before the finish of the fight
When the panting wolf shakes free
From the bloody corpse, and he
Lies like a sack, defaced and dead,
And the sheep into the hills are fled
And the wolf slinks to his bed.

Now the *Jervis Bay* is ablaze. The fo'c'sle is blown away.
Splinters rive her decks to ribbons and bury her under spray,
And her burning hull as she plunged on was a bright torch
        that day.
She shudders. With the clearing smoke her main bridge is
        gone,
And Fegen's arm is a shredded stump, and he fights on.
He staggers aft to the docking bridge. Another blinding blast.
The Ensign down. 'Another Ensign! Nail it to the mast.'

A seaman climbs and nails it there, where the House Flag used
    to fly,
And there it speaks defiance to the shaker of the sky.
He strives to climb to the after bridge, but it is unavailing,
One arm and half the shoulder gone, and strength fast failing.
But there is still the after gun that he can bring to bear.
'Independent fire!' he cries, as heaves into the air
The after bridge. He lives, and staggers forrard again, before
The rolling smoke envelops him, and he is seen no more.
Now her engines had ceased to turn, but still the shells came
    pouring,
Till with a roar her boilers burst, and the white steam went
    soaring
Away to the sky. Her back was broken, and she was settling
    fast,
And the fire blazed, and the smoke-pall brooded like a banyan
    vast,
But still the torn Ensign flew from the black stump mast
And the after gun was firing still and asking no quarter
When the hot barrel hissed into the wild grey water.

So ended the fight of the *Scheer* and the *Jervis Bay*.
That for twenty vital minutes drew the raider's fire that day,
When of the convoy's thirty-seven, thirty-three went safe
    away
And home at last to England came, without the *Jervis Bay*.

But now thick night was over the sea, and a wind from the
    west blew keen,
And the hopeless waters tossed their heads where the *Jervis
Bay* had been,
And the raider was lost in the rain and the night, and low
    clouds hid the seas,
But high above sea and storm and cloud appeared the galaxies,
And the big stars called the little stars that had not dared to
    peep,
And all the stars of heaven came out across the heaving deep,
And they shone bright over the good shepherd of sheep.

Index of first lines

133

Acknowledgments

Acknowledgments for permission to reprint copyright poems are due to the following authors, executors and publishers:

the authors' representatives and Sidgwick and Jackson Ltd. for a poem from *Walls and Hedges* by J. Redwood Anderson, and a poem from *Verses* by E. Hilton Young; the Postmaster-General for *Night Mail* by W. H. Auden; the author's executors for *The Hippo* by Hilaire Belloc; Gerald Duckworth & Co. Ltd. for a poem from *Cautionary Tales for Children* by Hilaire Belloc; the authors for *Nancy Hanks* by Rosemary Benét, *The Ballad of William Sycamore* by Stephen Vincent Benét, and Mrs. William Rose Benét for *Jesse James* by the late William Rose Benét; David Higham Associates Ltd. for Charles Causley's poems *Cowboy Song* and *Death of an Aircraft*; the author and the Oxford University Press for *A Ballad to Queen Elizabeth (of the Spanish Armada)* by Austin Dobson; the author and Faber & Faber Ltd. for a poem from *Old Possum's Book of Practical Cats* by T. S. Eliot; the author for *Head and Heart* by C. D. B. Ellis; Eleanor Farjeon and J. M. Dent & Sons Ltd. for a poem from *Kings and Queens* by Eleanor and Herbert Farjeon; Jonathan

Cape Ltd. and Holt, Rinehart and Winston Inc. for Robert Frost's poem *Out, Out* from *The Poetry of Robert Frost*; the author for *The Ice-Cart* by Wilfred Gibson; Bernard Gilhooly for *At 30,000 ft*; the author for *Electric Love* by Denis Glover; the author and Macmillan & Co. Ltd. for a poem from *Poems* by Ralph Hodgson; the literary representative of the trustees of the estate of the late A. E. Housman and Jonathan Cape Ltd. for two poems from the *Collected Poems* of A. E. Housman; Faber & Faber Ltd. for Ted Hughes' *An Otter* from *Lupercal*, Seamus Heaney's *Mid Term Break* from *Death of a Naturalist* and Edwin Muir's *The Castle* from *Collected Poems 1921–1958*; Mrs. George Bambridge, Macmillan & Co. Ltd. and the Macmillan Company of Canada for *A Smuggler's Song* from *Puck of Pook's Hill* by Rudyard Kipling; the author and the Macmillan Company, New York, for two poems from the *Collected Poems* of Vachel Lindsay; *The New York Herald Tribune* and the parents of the late John Gillespie Magee Jr. for *High Flight*; Doubleday & Company Inc., New York, for a poem from *Poems and Portraits* by Don Marquis, copyright 1922 by Doubleday & Company Inc.; the author, the Society of Authors and the Macmillan Company, New York, for *Spanish Waters* by Dr. John Masefield, O.M.; Dobson Book Ltd. for Spike Milligan's *On the Ning Nang Nong* from *Silly Verse for Kids*; the author and J. M. Dent & Sons for *The Lama* and *Song to be Sung by the Fathers of Infant Female Children* by Ogden Nash; the executors of the late Sir Henry Newbolt and John Murray (Publishers) Ltd. for two poems from *Poems New and Old* by Sir Henry Newbolt; the author and William Blackwood & Sons Ltd. for a poem from the *Collected Poems of Alfred Noyes*; the authors and Jonathan Cape Ltd. for a poem from *A Map of Verona* by Henry Reed and for a poem from *The Flaming Terrapin* by Roy Campbell; Mrs. Stephens and Macmillan & Co Ltd. for a poem from the *Collected Poems* of James Stephens; the author and Putman & Co. Ltd. for an extract from *The 'Jervis Bay'* by Michael Thwaites; Burns, Oates and Washbourne Ltd. for *Picardie* by Alys Fane Trotter from *Nigel and Other Poems*; *Night Bombers* is reprinted by permission of *Punch*.

The cover shows a photograph of the painting *The 'Victory' at Trafalgar* by J. M. W. Turner, reproduced by courtesy of the National Maritime Museum, Greenwich Hospital Collection.